NED SMITH'S
WILDLIFE
SKETCHBOOK

NATIONAL WILDLIFE FEDERATION

Ned Smith was a self-taught naturalist, writer, photographer, illustrator and artist who was good at virtually everything he did. And he enjoyed it all with a gusto that was contagious.

Pennsylvanian E. Stanley "Ned" Smith had already made his mark as a wildlife artist at Pennsylvania *Game News*, the state's wildlife conservation magazine, long before I became its editor in 1961. Ned had been acting editor of *Game News* during the Korean War and he illustrated and wrote a great many of the nature articles published in *Game News* from the late 1940s to the middle 1980s. His columns, "Walking Shoes" and "Gone for the Day," were classics among modern day nature writings. I coaxed from Ned as many color covers as he would paint. I also talked Ned into repainting the set of four wildlife charts originally created by Jacob Bates Abbott.

Ned Smith was so good at depicting wildlife behavior with pen and brush and at writing about what he illustrated that he was a natural to contribute to the pages of *National Wildlife* magazine.

When I became managing editor of *National Wildife* in 1965, Ned Smith began producing his "Wildlife Sketchbooks." The columns, many of which are featured in this book, gave *National Wildlife* readers a fascinating insight into the world of nature.

From the middle 1960s to his death in 1985, Ned's work also appeared in *National Geographic*, *Natural History*, National Audubon Society publications, and nearly every sporting and hunting magazine in the country. He illustrated 14 books, including a Peterson *Field Guide to Birds' Nests* by Hal Harrison; *The Complete Book of the Wild Turkey* by Roger Latham; *Billfish* by Charles Mather; and *Ecology and Field Biology*, a textbook.

During his last 10 years, Ned concentrated less on illustrating articles and books and more on producing large paintings depicting a variety of wildlife species in their natural habitats. Many believe that Ned did his finest work during this period of his life and purchased Ned's paintings to adorn their homes and offices. A collection of his work is also in the Carnegie-Mellon Institute Museum, Pittsburgh.

As a friend and colleague of Ned Smith for more than 25 years, I was impressed by his capacity to observe and record the natural world. His talent was in his ability to express these observations accurately, in both the written word and in art, just as they appeared in nature.

Some of my most memorable days afield were with Ned Smith hunting deer in Huntingdon County, Pennsylvania, fishing for bass on that state's Juniata River, and watching the hawk migrations at Cape May, New Jersey.

Ned constantly recorded either on paper or film a great deal of what he saw. At the end of his career, he had about 40,000 slides in his files. I'll never forget the disagreement we had in the early 1960s over the best film for magazine reproduction— Kodachrome or Ektachrome.

Ned, of course, was right about Kodachrome, which became the standard for quality magazine photography around the world.

On April 22, 1985, Ned Smith died at the age of 65. His last moments were typical of his whole life. He was planting a garden with his beloved wife, Marie, in their yard in Millersburg, Pennsylvania. Ned's whole life was spent planting the seeds of love and understanding for nature. This book is a reflection of that life's work.

—George H. Harrison
Hubertus, Wisconsin

Cover Photo by Jerry Mesmer, Adams Studio

Design by Eason Associates, Inc.

Library of Congress CIP Data

Smith, Ned.
    Ned Smith's wildlife sketchbook.

    Includes index.
    1. Natural history. 2. Zoology.
I. Title.
II. Title: Wildlife sketchbook.
H45.5.S58   1988   508   88-12534
ISBN 0-912186-94-1

CONTENTS

SPRING

It will be a gradual transformation, but so gradual no one can say just when a brown field becomes green.

Mid-winter is mating and house-hunting time, and the mated pair travels widely, searching for the most suitable hole to re-model. The pair usually readies an extra den or two in case they are needed later.

The pups, usually four to eight, are born in early spring. At about six weeks of age they begin venturing out of the den to play, nurse, or eat food regurgitated by the parents.

LIFE IN A FOX DEN

Bambi and The Three Bears to the contrary, most mammals do not rear their young in family groups that include Father. The male's responsibility usually ends with the impregnation of the female (or females). More often than not, he assumes no part in rearing the young. He does not display concern for his mate or his offspring. But red foxes are delightfully different.

The male and female fox are a devoted couple, thought by many to mate for life. Both take an interest in establishing the nursery den and in feeding and training the pups. The male doesn't occupy the den, but he is seldom far away. His watchful eyes miss little and his warning bark is often the first sign of danger. Few animals exhibit deeper distress when misfortune befalls the family.

Of course, foxes aren't per-fect. They have been known to embark on killing orgies at the sight of a pen full of squeaking, wildly fluttering pullets.

But the watcher at the den sees a better side—the playful nature of the captivating pups, the patience of the vixen who tolerates their mauling with equanimity, and the quiet pride of the male as he drops a mouse or rabbit before them. It's even possible to see the foxes outwit a snoopy dog in the neighborhood, or to watch them move the entire family to another den if disturbed, taking with them the bone or stick that has been the pups' favorite plaything.

Unlike their gray cousins, red foxes do not like being underground. They will usually run before hounds all day and all night rather than hole up. They even prefer curling up on the snow to napping underground.

The only time a burrow is commonly used is when pups need shelter. However, the youngsters seem eager to sam-

ple the exciting sunlit world on the outside. At ten weeks of age, they have already explored much of the nearby terrain and, by summer's end, they will have left for good. Long-legged and headstrong, each will have gone its own way. The abandoned den will await its next occupants in unaccustomed silence.

Should human intrusion or parasites make the old den untenable, the pups are carried or led to one of the reserve dens.

Most dens have more than one entrance. This one has an "escape hatch" concealed in the nearby high grass.

The male lives apart, but brings food to the vixen and young. As the pups grow older they are coaxed farther from the den, taught to find food and to catch living prey that is first disabled by the parent.

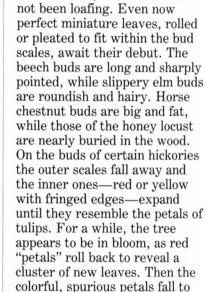

Skunk cabbage

Hickory bud

Mayapple

THE GREENING OF A WOODLAND

A few months ago, I watched the woods here in my home state, Pennsylvania, fill up with snow. Now, with the snow scarcely gone, they are about to fill up again—this time with green. It will be a complete transformation, but so gradual that no one can say just when a brown field becomes green.

My favorite spot for watching spring take over is a swampy woodland close to the river. Here, where dark water reflects the surrounding trees, the striped and mottled hoods of the skunk cabbage rise through the waterlogged leaves.

When the skunk cabbage first appears in midwinter, it is the earliest of wild flowers, for each hood shelters a spadix of flowers. Hoods that appear later are accompanied by young leaves tightly rolled into pointed horns that easily poke through the overlying duff and muck.

Nearby hummocks are capped with dead cinnamon ferns. Brown with age and flattened by winter snows, each sprawling tuft shelters a cluster of buds. The buds are clothed in the silky down that protected them all during the winter from transpiration—the loss of water vapor through leaf surfaces.

A month from now, the tight buds will rise above the ground to become the familiar "fiddleheads," before slowly uncoiling to form feathery fronds.

By winter's end, buds on the spicebushes had swollen into round, yellowish balls. The first spell of warm weather popped them open, covering the twigs with tiny lemon-yellow flowers, followed in a week by a haze of small green leaves.

Beneath the spicebushes is the barest, most somber-looking soil this side of the river, with no hint of better things to come. And yet, when the time is right, hundreds of greenish-purple points emerge from as many starch-filled bulbs. They are the new leaves of the trout lily, or yellow adder's tongue, soon to cover the drab expanse of earth with paired, mottled leaves and butter-colored flowers.

Like bronzy-green fingers, masses of mayapple shoots will come poking through other bare patches. Each shoot consists of a stem surmounted by a large leaf. But to expedite the emerging, the leaves have been wrapped around their stalks and enclosed in a sheath that looks like a folded umbrella in a case.

As their height increases, the "umbrellas" open. The mayapple plants will later shelter a single waxy, white flower.

Cinnamon fern fiddleheads

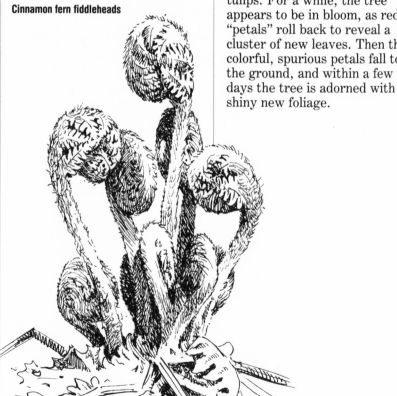

Meanwhile, the trees have not been loafing. Even now perfect miniature leaves, rolled or pleated to fit within the bud scales, await their debut. The beech buds are long and sharply pointed, while slippery elm buds are roundish and hairy. Horse chestnut buds are big and fat, while those of the honey locust are nearly buried in the wood. On the buds of certain hickories the outer scales fall away and the inner ones—red or yellow with fringed edges—expand until they resemble the petals of tulips. For a while, the tree appears to be in bloom, as red "petals" roll back to reveal a cluster of new leaves. Then the colorful, spurious petals fall to the ground, and within a few days the tree is adorned with shiny new foliage.

THOSE CRAZY HAMMERHEADS

Pileated woodpecker

Rumors persist throughout the southeastern United States about the possible existence of the spectacular ivory-billed woodpecker. But just as interesting are the other 21 woodpecker species indigenous to North America and Canada.

One thing shared by all of them, from the six-inch downy woodpecker to the twenty-inch ivory-bill, is the propensity to peck wood. Most extract the bulk of their food—insects, larvae, and insect eggs—from tree bark crevices, from beneath the bark itself, or from burrows within the wood. All woodpeckers nest in cavities they hew from trunks, posts, or poles. The crow-sized pileated woodpecker, for instance, carves out a cavity up to eight inches in diameter and two feet deep!

It is their specialization for pecking that makes these birds so interesting. Nature has fitted woodpeckers with a straight, sturdy, often chisel-shaped bill. It is backed by a skull that is exceptionally hard and thick for a bird. To anchor them while they work, woodpeckers have powerful feet with three or four strongly curved, opposing claws. And the tail, which serves as a prop, is tipped with stiff, sharp barbs that won't slip on the slickest bark. For reaching borers in their innermost galleries, the woodpecker has a slender, extensible tongue with a spear-like tip.

So much stretch could not be built into the usual bird tongue that is attached at the rear of the mouth. Instead, the woodpecker's tongue forks into a pair of bony bases that loop behind the skull, pass over the top, and are rooted in one nostril! This bony fork is thought to have evolved from the gill arches of a remote ancestor.

A few woodpeckers with non-typical tastes have non-typical tongues to match. Sapsuckers are fond of sap which they get by pecking rows of holes through the bark of trees. A brush-like tongue neatly laps up the sweet drops. Flickers are fond of ants, which

Ivory-billed woodpecker

Downy woodpecker

they collect with long tongues coated with a sticky saliva.

Few parts of the country are without their woodpeckers. The hairy woodpecker is a permanent resident throughout the entire United States and most of Canada. His diminutive look-alike, the downy, occupies nearly as much territory, while the yellow-bellied sapsucker is known throughout all but northernmost North America as either a resident or a migrant. The well-known yellow-shafted flicker of the East is replaced in the West by the similar red-shafted flicker.

The huge black and white pileated woodpecker with his scarlet crest is found in heavily forested areas; the much smaller red, black and white red-headed woodpecker is at home in small groves of trees in the prairie states. The yellow capped three-toed woodpeckers and the striking white-headed woodpecker haunt western evergreen forests, while both the gilded flicker and the Gila woodpecker make their nest holes in the saguaro cactus of the desert—evidence that wherever there are trees or tree substitutes you will find woodpeckers.

Flicker (showing interior of nest)

A PRIMER FOR BIRDWATCHERS

Birds are made for watching. They live nearly everywhere, they run the gamut from cute to elegant, and some are as colorful as flowers. You can easily observe their feeding, their fighting and their mating displays from a kitchen window or a hiking trail.

A good deal of bird watching is done with only the naked eye, but binoculars are indispensable to really appreciate a bird's beauty and to distinguish obscure identification marks. The beginner can profit by buying a 7 power 35mm binocular, which means that it magnifies seven times the diameter of the original and has 35mm objective lenses. More powerful glasses are available, but their greater magnification makes a user's unsteadiness show up even more; the larger lenses are also bulkier and heavier.

The only other necessity for bird watching is a field guide.

For many years, *A Field Guide to the Birds* and its companion, *A Field Guide to Western Birds*, both by Roger Tory Peterson, were the field identification bibles. In recent years, *Birds of North America* by Robbins, Bruun, Zim and Singer, covering both eastern and western North America in one volume, has also become popular.*

Whichever field guide you buy will help you learn what birds to expect in your area during each season. You can also memorize field marks—identifying features that must often be recognized in the brief time you have a bird in view.

Later, you might add more equipment. A telescope of at least 20 power will reveal astonishing details, but must be held steady with a tripod, a beanbag or a gunstock. Bird song recordings are useful for learning to recognize the sounds birds make. You might want to build portable blinds from which to observe birds at close range.

Seeing a bird is one thing, but identifying it can be another thing altogether. Beginners may often look for the wrong characteristics—meaningless features that are shared by many birds.

Try to establish the size of the bird by comparing it to a familiar species. Is it as large as a wren, a house sparrow, a robin, a crow? Notice its conformation. Is it long and slender, short and plump, long-necked, or long-legged? Among some similar species, the shape of the tail tip is important.

Of utmost significance is the shape of the bill. Whether it is short and stout, short and slender, long and curved or broad and flattened is important in

assigning it to a family—a step that will make final identification of the bird easier.

Make a mental note of the bird's general color, and try to distinguish wing bars, tail markings, breast streaking, eye rings or crests. When comparing your specimen with the book's pictures and descriptions, check for seasonal, sex and age differences. Try to remember the bird's song or call notes: these are essential for positive identification of some look-alike species. Note clues such as habitat, flight characteristics, nesting habits and season of occurrence.

Identification is only the beginning in meaningful birding. While you have the bird under observation, try to learn as much as you can about it; when you come in from the field, read and find out even more.

Finding new species becomes more difficult once you have identified the ubiquitous house sparrow, starling, grackle and robin. Remember that varied habitat produces varied inhabitants. The edge where a wood lot gives way to an abandoned field might yield woodpeckers, thrushes and warblers from the woods, and vesper sparrows, redwings and barn swallows from the farmland. Catbirds, buntings and cardinals inhabit the brushy transitional strip. The junctures of salt marsh and dune or lake and shoreline are well worth investigating, too.

Birds are easiest to approach where they are accustomed to human activity. National parks and national wildlife refuges are

*Ed. note: Since this column was written in 1977, several more good guides have been published, among them *The National Geographic Society Field Guide to the Birds of North America* and Audubon's three-volume set, *The Audubon Society Guides to North American Birds*.

obvious spots. However, don't forget state parks, national monuments, picnic areas, roadside rests, boat docks and golf courses. Ski lifts that operate in summer for tourists can transport you to the high country of the rosy finches and the ptarmigan. Check patches of snow for insects and the birds that eat them. Boat trips for tourists can produce some outstanding bird-watching experiences.

And there are bird sanctuaries (resorts that cater to birders) and such well-known birding meccas as Pennsylvania's Hawk Mountain, Tucson's Arizona-Sonoran Desert Museum, and Florida's Wakulla Springs.
and Florida's Wakulla Springs.

You can attract birds to your home territory by feeding them in winter, growing food-bearing plants, erecting birdhouses, and putting out nesting material. Decoys on ponds and marshes beckon to migrating waterfowl, and owl decoys bring in crows, jays and hawks. Recordings of various bird voices are un-

surpassed for calling in the same species or, in the case of certain owl recordings, excitable prey species. A hissing "pshhh, pshhh, pshhh"—forcefully whispered—often brings curious birds out of hiding.

Dress inconspicuously when birding. Move slowly, preferably with the sun at your back, listening for bird sounds and watching for movement. During the spring migration and the later courtship season, you'll locate lots of males by their singing. Learn also the nonvocal sounds of a drumming grouse, a winnowing snipe, or a booming nighthawk. Track down every unknown sound; even a simple "chip" can reveal a new species.

The fussing of anxious birds is often a clue to the presence of eggs or young. Yet be patient. When their nervousness subsides they usually return to the nest, revealing its location. But do your nest watching from afar; a disturbance near the nest often results in nesting failure.

By becoming a careful observer, you're bound to enjoy birding. And with nearly 700 species of birds in North America above Mexico, there's little danger you'll grow tired of seeing the same old stuff.

Imaginary bird showing common field marks

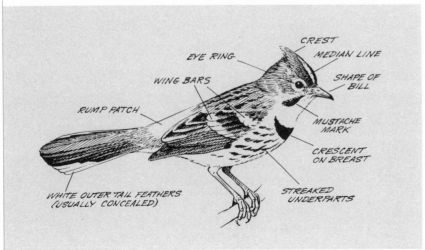

CREST
EYE RING
MEDIAN LINE
WING BARS
SHAPE OF BILL
RUMP PATCH
MUSTACHE MARK
CRESCENT ON BREAST
WHITE OUTER TAIL FEATHERS (USUALLY CONCEALED)
STREAKED UNDERPARTS

Sighting a rare Peregrine falcon *(right)* or the Bachman's warbler *(below)* would delight any birdwatcher.

Some species, like the chickadee *(above)* and meadowlark *(left)*, are best identified by their distinctive songs.

INDEPENDENT NESTLINGS

I f the young of ground-nesting gamebirds, shorebirds, and waterfowl were as helpless as those of robins and sparrows, few would survive in their exposed situations. Instead they are bright-eyed, clothed in down, and able to scurry about shortly after hatching. Scientists call this self-sufficiency *precocialism*. Helpless nestlings are called *altricial*.

The differences between the two kinds of birds encompass more than the nestlings themselves. The eggs of precocial birds are larger than altricial ones to accommodate the more completely developed embryo. Because the young leave the nest soon after hatching, the nests of precocial birds can be as simple as the tern's sparsely lined hollow in the sand or the ruffed grouse's leafy depression.

When the precocial bird's time has arrived, it cuts away the big end of the shell with the "egg-tooth" on its bill and then squirms free. Within half an hour it is standing on sturdy legs, eyes open and downy duds dry and fluffy.

Because the nest and its discarded eggshells attract predators, the mother soon leads her brood from the scene.

The young birds react to danger instinctively. Turkeys, grouse, and quail scatter and "hit the dirt" on command, their dead leaf camouflage rendering

If colored like their black and white parents, newly hatched stilts would be too obvious to the eyes of predators. Instead, their colors match the bare ground of their usual haunts.

If they are discovered in spite of their hiding ability, those long legs are put to good use. Their escape is usually covered by a bold and extremely vocal aerial attack by their mother.

them practically invisible. When more than a few days old, leggy birdlings like killdeer and stilts often opt to outrun their pursuers. Wild ducklings scamper across the water with amazing speed, hiding ashore or diving if closely pressed. Upland game birds soon learn to fly; grouse can flutter to low branches at the tender age of two weeks.

For the nestlings, even feeding is largely instinctive, though the hen does encourage them to make the proper selections. Before long, brooding in cold or rainy weather is the only essential activity that remains for the devoted mother.

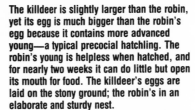

Egg-tooth

Killdeer's egg

Robin's egg

Young precocial birds, such as this pheasant chick, need only to flatten themselves against the ground to become almost invisible. Many won't move even when picked up, so complete is their faith in nature's camouflage.

The killdeer is slightly larger than the robin, yet its egg is much bigger than the robin's egg because it contains more advanced young—a typical precocial hatchling. The robin's young is helpless when hatched, and for nearly two weeks it can do little but open its mouth for food. The killdeer's eggs are laid on the stony ground; the robin's in an elaborate and sturdy nest.

Frightened baby wood ducks hurry to keep up with their mother. If threatened, many wild duck hens thrash the water with their wings, feigning injury while the ducklings scramble ashore and hide in the vegetation.

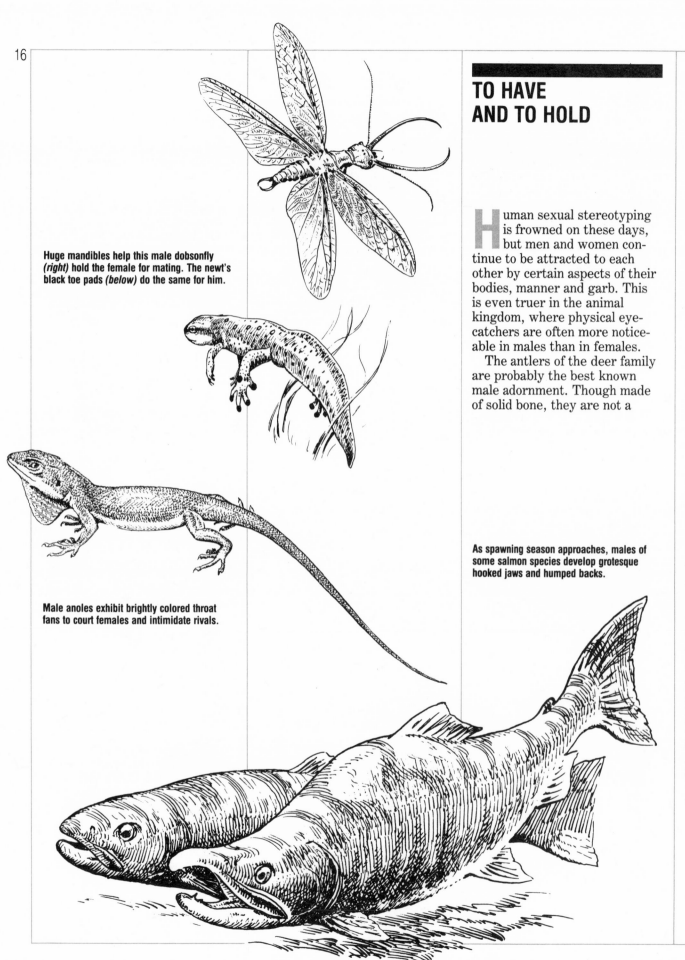

Huge mandibles help this male dobsonfly *(right)* **hold the female for mating. The newt's black toe pads** *(below)* **do the same for him.**

Male anoles exhibit brightly colored throat fans to court females and intimidate rivals.

As spawning season approaches, males of some salmon species develop grotesque hooked jaws and humped backs.

TO HAVE AND TO HOLD

Human sexual stereotyping is frowned on these days, but men and women continue to be attracted to each other by certain aspects of their bodies, manner and garb. This is even truer in the animal kingdom, where physical eye-catchers are often more noticeable in males than in females.

The antlers of the deer family are probably the best known male adornment. Though made of solid bone, they are not a permanent extension of the bony cranium, as are the bony cores of the horns on cattle, sheep and goats. Each summer the bull moose, the bull elk and the buck deer grow the antlers as armament for their contests with rival males. Once the fall rutting season has passed, a hormonal shift causes the antlers to drop from their moorings.

The spurs that protrude from the legs of male turkeys and pheasants serve a similar purpose. Clashing cock pheasants leap into the air and try to rake each other with these weapons.

For many species, mating happens only after the suitor instinctively performs a series of courtship rituals. A painted turtle excites his mate by stroking the female's cheeks with the elongated claws on his forefeet. The male fiddler crab seduces his partner by waving an enlarged claw before her face. The gesture can hardly be ignored, especially in the case of some species whose "fiddle" claw constitutes nearly half the male's total weight. The female's claws are normally proportioned.

The ruffed grouse spreads his tail to form a handsome fan, raises a ruff of glossy feathers around his neck and struts in pompous splendor. The turkey gobbler also struts, enhancing his performance with enormously swollen scarlet wattles and iridescent body feathers standing on end. He wears spurs on sturdy shanks and a long tuft of hairlike feathers sprouts from his breast. Called a beard, this structure's purpose is anyone's guess but it is almost exclusively a male appendage.

Animals produce many kinds of audible warnings to other

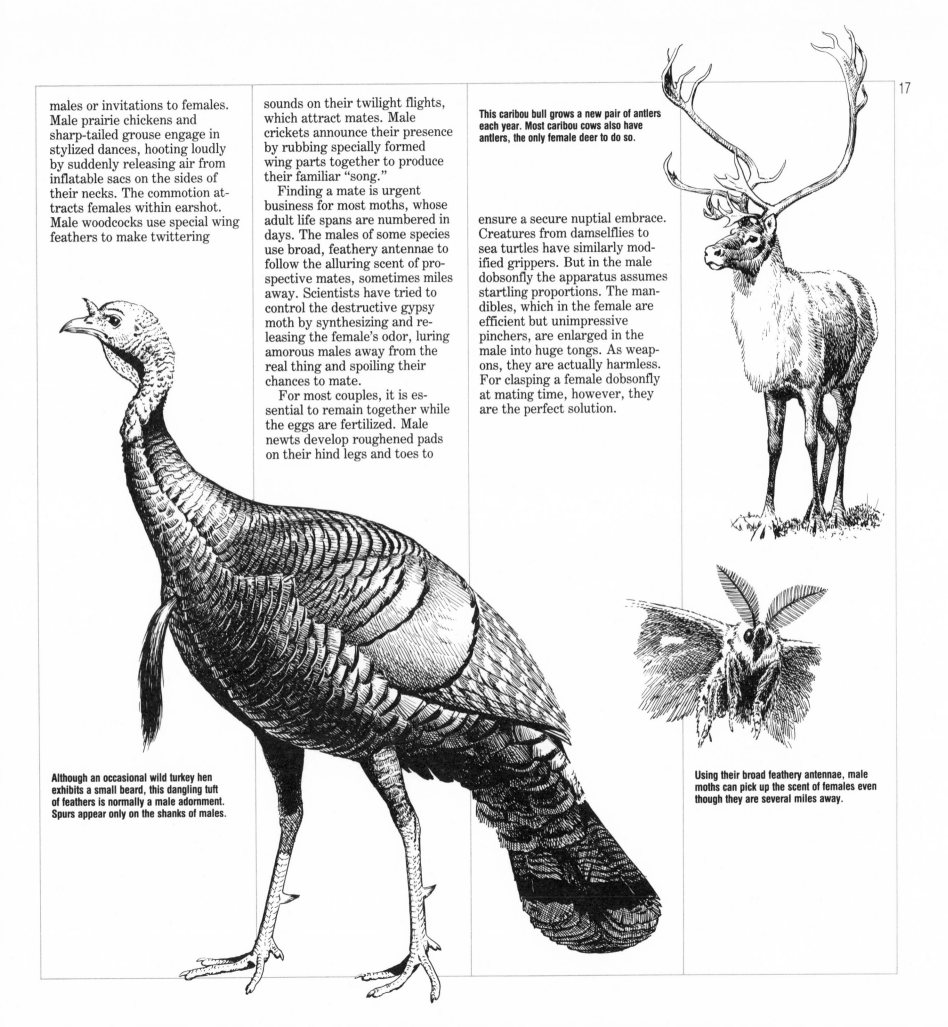

males or invitations to females. Male prairie chickens and sharp-tailed grouse engage in stylized dances, hooting loudly by suddenly releasing air from inflatable sacs on the sides of their necks. The commotion attracts females within earshot. Male woodcocks use special wing feathers to make twittering sounds on their twilight flights, which attract mates. Male crickets announce their presence by rubbing specially formed wing parts together to produce their familiar "song."

Finding a mate is urgent business for most moths, whose adult life spans are numbered in days. The males of some species use broad, feathery antennae to follow the alluring scent of prospective mates, sometimes miles away. Scientists have tried to control the destructive gypsy moth by synthesizing and releasing the female's odor, luring amorous males away from the real thing and spoiling their chances to mate.

For most couples, it is essential to remain together while the eggs are fertilized. Male newts develop roughened pads on their hind legs and toes to ensure a secure nuptial embrace. Creatures from damselflies to sea turtles have similarly modified grippers. But in the male dobsonfly the apparatus assumes startling proportions. The mandibles, which in the female are efficient but unimpressive pinchers, are enlarged in the male into huge tongs. As weapons, they are actually harmless. For clasping a female dobsonfly at mating time, however, they are the perfect solution.

This caribou bull grows a new pair of antlers each year. Most caribou cows also have antlers, the only female deer to do so.

Although an occasional wild turkey hen exhibits a small beard, this dangling tuft of feathers is normally a male adornment. Spurs appear only on the shanks of males.

Using their broad feathery antennae, male moths can pick up the scent of females even though they are several miles away.

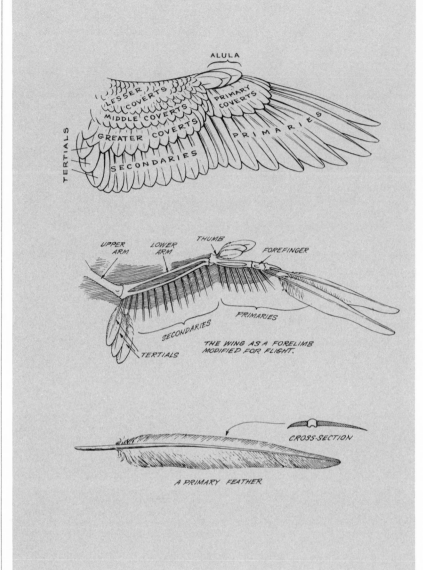

Long, pointed primaries enable the swift *(below)* to live up to its name. The albatross's 11-foot wingspan *(above)* is mostly airfoil, which allows high-speed gliding.

HOW BIRDS FLY

irds have different flight characteristics, but the basic magic that keeps them in the air is the same. When an eagle leaps from its lofty perch, the first powerful thrust of each wing and the quill-stiffened tips of each primary bite the air at an angle, driving the bird forward. On the upstroke, the wings bend and the primaries open louvers to lessen air resistance, while the rearward flip of the wings adds another forward thrust. Another downstroke cleaves the air, then another, and the big bird is on its way.

Once airborne, less effort is needed, for most of the "lift" is now provided by the airfoil shape of the wings. Because air flowing over the curved upper surface must travel faster than that passing beneath the flat undersurface, an area of low pressure is created above the

Although ill-suited for sustained rapid flight, the grouse's short, rounded wings make possible a quick takeoff and exceptional maneuverability in dense underbrush.

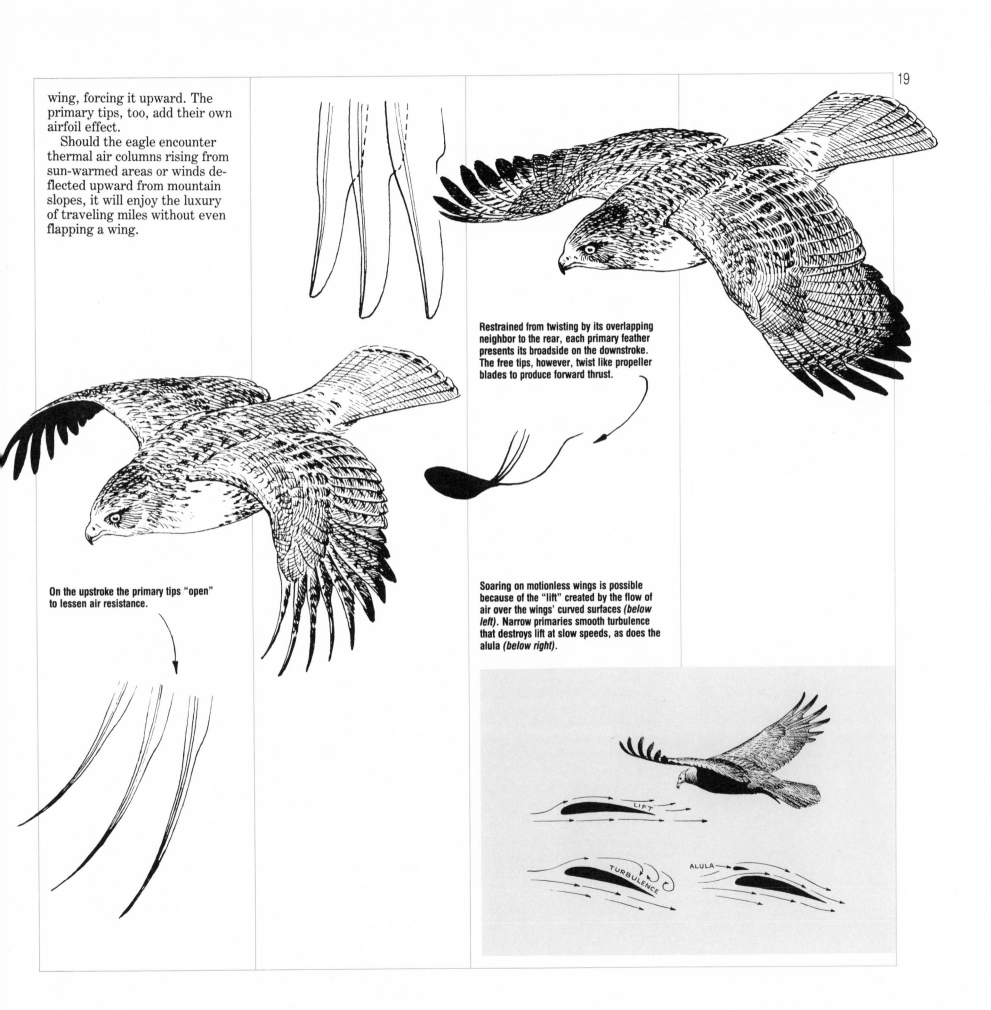

wing, forcing it upward. The primary tips, too, add their own airfoil effect.

Should the eagle encounter thermal air columns rising from sun-warmed areas or winds deflected upward from mountain slopes, it will enjoy the luxury of traveling miles without even flapping a wing.

Restrained from twisting by its overlapping neighbor to the rear, each primary feather presents its broadside on the downstroke. The free tips, however, twist like propeller blades to produce forward thrust.

On the upstroke the primary tips "open" to lessen air resistance.

Soaring on motionless wings is possible because of the "lift" created by the flow of air over the wings' curved surfaces (*below left*). **Narrow primaries smooth turbulence that destroys lift at slow speeds, as does the alula** (*below right*).

LIFT

TURBULENCE

ALULA

BIRD BILLS DESIGNED FOR USE

From the time a baby bird chips its way out of the egg with a spur on its bill called an "egg tooth," the bill will play a vital role in the bird's life. With it the bird will fight off enemies, build its nest, turn its eggs, gather its food, and feed its young. More than mere substitutes for hands, bills become tweezers, chisels, hammers, spears, knives, nutcrackers, and even insect traps.

Food habits and bill design are inseparable. Goat-suckers, swifts, and swallows have insignificant bills, but their huge mouths literally open "from ear to ear" to snatch flying insects.

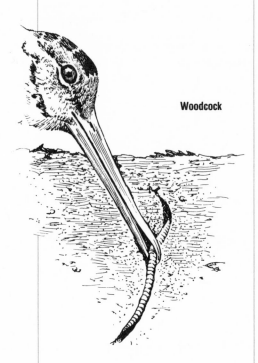

Woodcock

Many are fringed with bristles to prevent the insects' escape.

Brown creepers, in contrast, pick tiny insects, insect eggs, and pupae from crevices in tree bark. Their bills resemble slender, curved tweezers.

Sandpipers, curlews, snipes, ibises, and other wading birds need longer forceps for pulling worms and crustaceans from sand or mud. The woodcock's bill—more than one-fourth of his total length—makes an effective probe for earthworms. It not only feels the unseen worm, but it also can be opened at the tip, the upper mandible crooking like a finger to grip the slippery prey.

Hummingbirds' bills, long in proportion to their bodies, are needle-thin, ideal for extracting nectar and minute insects from the deep spurs and throats of honeysuckle, jewelweed, columbine, and similar flowers.

Woodpeckers' straight bills, on the other hand, are incredibly powerful. Driven by triphammer blows, the chisel-like bill of a pileated woodpecker can cut through three inches of solid wood in minutes to uncover and withdraw a borer. The most impressive evidence of this bird's woodworking ability, however, is its nest—a cavity seven inches in diameter and up to two feet deep, chiseled out of the heart of a large forest tree.

Seed-eating finches' conical bills vary from the sharply pointed nibs of the diminutive pine siskins to the massive, ivory-colored mandibles of the

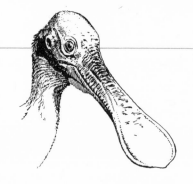

Roseate spoonbill

evening grosbeak. All finches have relatively powerful bills, but my bird banding friends use their gloves when handling an evening grosbeak. Those mandibles can quickly chop up a frozen apple, and human fingers offer less resistance.

Strangest of all the finch bills are the overlapping mandibles of the crossbills. A crossbill inserts its bill between the scales of pine and spruce cones, deftly prying the scales apart so its tongue can scoop out seeds.

Many birds like shellfish, but opening them can be a problem. Gulls break the shells of clams by dropping them on bridges, roads, or hard beaches from a height of 20 or 30 feet. Scoters and eider ducks swallow clams and oysters whole, depending upon their powerful gizzards to crush the shells. However, oyster catchers have thin, blade-like bills that slip between the shell halves and immobilize the clam. The rare Everglades kite guides its hooked bill into the spirals of freshwater snails to extract the succulent inhabitants.

A wealth of insects and small crustaceans hides beneath small stones and shells on beaches and flats. Aware of this bounty, the turnstone flips over every movable object it encounters with its flattened, upturned bill.

Many unrelated birds have surprisingly similar beaks and employ them in similar ways.

The small duck called the shoveller swings its spoon-shaped bill from side to side as it swims, opening and closing it rapidly. When the mandibles close on some item of food, water is ejected through hundreds of tiny grooves, or lamellae, which strain out the desired object.

Although their talons are their real weapons, birds of prey possess powerful hooked bills that can pierce the skull of their prey and tear the carcass to pieces. Owls can wrench the heads off their victims and swallow the heads whole, then gulp down the remainder in large pieces—a practice made easy by their huge, gaping mouths. Bones, feathers, and other indigestible remains are later ejected through the mouth in the form of large pellets.

Pelicans' spacious gular pouches are well known fish-catching aids. Unlike their brown cousins which dive for fish, white pelicans surround their prey in shallow water and scoop up the frantic fish as they try to escape. Both species regurgitate semi-digested fish into their pouches and permit the nestlings to gobble it from these natural chowder bowls.

Evening grosbeak

Red crossbill

THE ZANY COURTSHIP OF GROUSE

Among the zaniest performances in the bird world are the mating season antics employed by male members of the grouse clan to impress the females, intimidate other males, and establish a territory.

Cock prairie chickens, for instance, fight and display on established "booming grounds." With wings drooping, stubby tails erect, heads lowered, and long, pointed neck feathers standing upright above their heads like horns, they look as fierce as possible. Orange neck

Prairie chickens

Hen

Male sage grouse

Ruffed grouse drumming.

Cock bird displaying with air sacs inflated.

sacs are periodically inflated like miniature balloons, and with stamping feet each male rushes forward a few steps, stops, and expels the air from the sacs with a loud booming sound. Cackles and sudden leaps are essential parts of the ritual.

Their relatives, the sharptail grouse, dance with their heads bowed, tails pointed upward, and wings outstretched and quivering. Stamping their feet, they scamper this way and that, pattering around in circles, leaping into the air or over one another. They expand and deflate their purplish air sacs, making a hollow hooting sound.

The big cock sage grouse is more the dandy, posing with long tail feathers fanned, and inflated yellow air sacs hanging down over his breast.

Sooty grouse inflate yellow air sacs and hoot loudly from the crowns of tall trees. The closely related dusky grouse hoots softly from the ground. Spruce grouse "drum" with fluttering wingbeats while flying from one perch to another or while ascending a tree.

The most celebrated performance, however, is the drumming of the ruffed grouse.

Bracing himself with feet and tail on a log, he beats his wings sharply, beginning with slow, measured thumps that accelerate to a rolling crescendo, then suddenly cease. It sounds like a distant gasoline engine starting reluctantly, then stalling.

From colonial times people have disagreed on how the sound is produced. The motion picture camera finally established beyond doubt that the thuds are produced by the wings striking only the air itself.

Drumming announces to other cocks that this neck of the woods is taken, and at the same time attracts amorous females.

In the presence of a female the male raises his ruffs about his head like a glossy black collar, fans his tail, and struts pompously before the desired one. It is one of nature's most impressive courtship displays.

SUMMER

A fencerow's charm lies in its variety, so take it slowly and try to see it all.

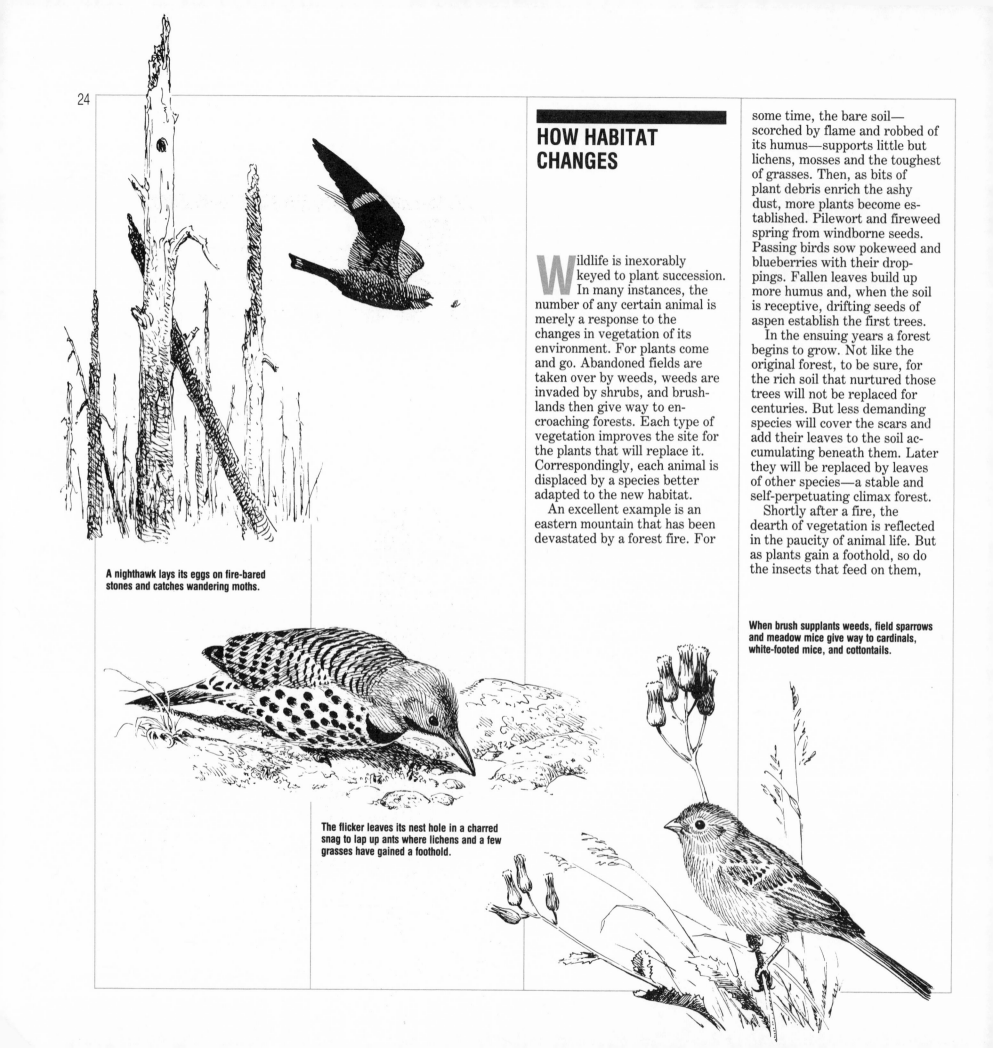

A nighthawk lays its eggs on fire-bared stones and catches wandering moths.

The flicker leaves its nest hole in a charred snag to lap up ants where lichens and a few grasses have gained a foothold.

HOW HABITAT CHANGES

Wildlife is inexorably keyed to plant succession. In many instances, the number of any certain animal is merely a response to the changes in vegetation of its environment. For plants come and go. Abandoned fields are taken over by weeds, weeds are invaded by shrubs, and brushlands then give way to encroaching forests. Each type of vegetation improves the site for the plants that will replace it. Correspondingly, each animal is displaced by a species better adapted to the new habitat.

An excellent example is an eastern mountain that has been devastated by a forest fire. For some time, the bare soil—scorched by flame and robbed of its humus—supports little but lichens, mosses and the toughest of grasses. Then, as bits of plant debris enrich the ashy dust, more plants become established. Pilewort and fireweed spring from windborne seeds. Passing birds sow pokeweed and blueberries with their droppings. Fallen leaves build up more humus and, when the soil is receptive, drifting seeds of aspen establish the first trees.

In the ensuing years a forest begins to grow. Not like the original forest, to be sure, for the rich soil that nurtured those trees will not be replaced for centuries. But less demanding species will cover the scars and add their leaves to the soil accumulating beneath them. Later they will be replaced by leaves of other species—a stable and self-perpetuating climax forest.

Shortly after a fire, the dearth of vegetation is reflected in the paucity of animal life. But as plants gain a foothold, so do the insects that feed on them,

When brush supplants weeds, field sparrows and meadow mice give way to cardinals, white-footed mice, and cottontails.

and then come the birds that eat the insects. As cover improves, meadow mice find places to tunnel and feed, and weasels, in turn, find good hunting.

The first brush attracts the first cottontail. As additional brushes choke out the weeds, warblers replace sparrows and towhees scratch for beetles where flickers once hunted ants. With the first trees, the ruffed grouse and whitetail deer show up, lured by the likelihood of nutritious buds. At last, the downy woodpeckers find trunks of ample girth for nesting.

As the trees grow more massive, their demands upon soil, water and sunlight spell death to the understory shrubs. Thicket-nesting birds disappear. Robbed of escape cover, rabbits and grouse grow scarce. With less available browse, fewer deer can survive the winters.

The forests have matured. Only those species adapted to a life among the big trees will thrive—until a fire, a storm, an insect infestation or a chain saw starts the cycle anew.

Brush and small trees provide food and cover for grouse and deer. But as forests mature, grouse cover is shaded out and deer can no longer reach twigs they need for food. Forest birds replace the thicket dwellers.

Unbroken expanse of old climax forest, like virgin forest, supports a wildlife population limited to those species needing large trees for nesting, denning, or food. Only over-mature trees provide dens for raccoons.

Wild turkeys, among others, find summer food more abundant where an occasional clearing lets in sunshine that promotes herbaceous growth and insect life.

Brown pelican, rare in Louisiana and Texas

Cottontails need cover.

WILDLIFE CONSERVATION

Humans have coexisted with wildlife in America for hundreds of years, but even today we are not sure if we are winning or losing the battle for wildlife conservation.

We no longer need fear the market hunter who exterminated the passenger pigeon and brought egrets and bison to the verge of extinction, although there is only a thin line between him and the poacher of alligators and waterfowl who is still with us. Today's sportsmen, better educated and guided by seasons and bag limits, are rarely a threat to a wildlife species.

We do, however, still have to contend with that ancient ogre, habitat destruction. In the old days it was the lumberman's axe and the forest fire which drove the wild turkey and the white-tail deer from the eastern forests and made mountain streams unlivable for the native brook trout. Today, it is the bulldozer which clears and levels wildlife habitat, filling in bays and marshes. And the result is much the same.

The mention of drainage makes conservationists shudder, for it, combined with drought, has destroyed innumerable waterfowl nesting areas and alarmingly reduced our prairie duck populations.

Dams sometimes have had the opposite effect, raising the water level and flooding areas used by wildlife. Streams and marshes disappear. Cold mountain streams often become warm water lakes; trout are replaced by bass and panfish.

Water pollution is an arch enemy of wildlife. Silt ruins spawning beds; decomposing wastes rob the water of oxygen; chemical wastes suffocate, starve, or just plain poison fish, frogs, and the aquatic insects upon which they feed. Thermal pollution, the by-product of steam and nuclear generating plants, kills wildlife by raising water temperatures to intolerable levels.

Pesticides are probably the most feared of all pollutants. They are accused of killing everything from robins to shellfish. They are prime suspects in the scarcity of bald eagles and ospreys in the Middle Atlantic states and the disappearance of the brown pelican from Texas and Louisiana. Not all states have outlawed the use of persistent, long-lasting pesticides and the federal government could still be more active in its regulation.*

Happily, some unexpected bonuses have come about by civilization's encroachment. The lumbering, which nearly finished off eastern big game, produced unprecedented numbers of thicket-loving grouse, whitetail deer, and rabbits when sprout growth became abundant. Strip farming seems to produce more pheasants than yesterday's small field farming. Farm ponds provide homes for bass and bluegills and feeding areas for swallows, wading birds, and waterfowl. Dams can release icy water from lake bottoms to provide superb trout fishing where none existed before. Squirrels, chipmunks, mourning doves, skunks, rabbits and pheasants thrive under the protection afforded them by some city ordinances.

We should treasure our wildlife populations and continue to upgrade the quality of their environment. By doing so, we ensure a livable environment for another species—called "man."

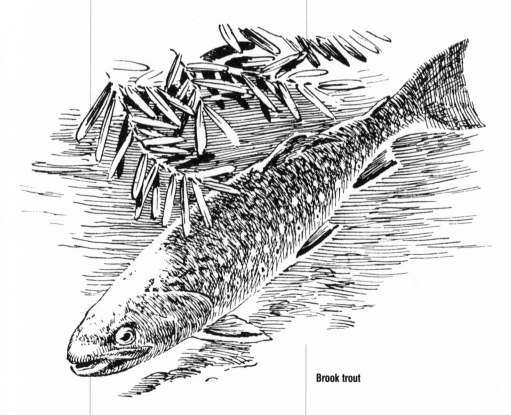

Brook trout

*Ed. note: Since this article was written in 1970, DDT use has been banned in the United States. In some areas of the country, ospreys, eagles, and pelicans—once diminishing—have made a comeback.

THE MICRO MURDERERS

Robber fly

Nothing could appear more benign than a field aglow with daisies, goldenrod and Queen Anne's lace. Yet, if a person moves slowly and looks closely among the flowers he will discover more carnage per square yard than on any battlefield. The violence is perpetrated by insects and other small creatures and it is all done to get food. Natural though it is, it leaves the observer thankful that insects come in small sizes.

Fix your eye on the platform of white flowers surmounting a Queen Anne's lace and note the traffic. Bees, wasps and beetles come and go. Some munch the flowers; others gather nectar or pollen. But many hope to eat their fellow visitors.

Wasps are the most abundant predators. In their egg-laying season they wander among the blossoms, each species seeking its natural prey. Some victimize only spiders; others, certain beetles; and still others, a particular larva. The victim is paralyzed by the wasp's sting and carried off to the egg chamber,

Dragonfly pursuing prey

Syrphid fly and flower spider

where it will nourish wasp larvae when they hatch.

One resident ogre is the ambush bug, a grotesque insect with a blocky head, an oddly flared body, and wide, flat forelegs that terminate in sinister spikes. Sphinxlike, it crouches among the flowers until the desired insect wanders within reach. Then the ambush bug's forelegs lash out, pinning down its victim. A pointed tube unfolds from under the head and penetrates the captive's body to drain it of its fluids.

Goldenrod flowers, too, witness their share of violence. They are apt to harbor crab-shaped flower spiders as well as predatory wasps and ambush bugs. Rather than spinning webs, these cunning *Arachnids* hide among the flowers and grab unsuspecting passersby. Even such formidable prey as bumblebees are quickly killed by the toxic bite of a flower spider.

The acres in bloom attract thousands of insects, which in turn draw predators. Several species of large dragonflies desert their ponds and streams in midsummer for better hunting in upland fields. Coursing back and forth on whirring wings, they can accelerate to 60 miles per hour to scoop up insects in the net formed by their bowed, bristly legs. Robber flies watch the activity from sunlit perches and launch themselves in swift pursuit of any appealing insect.

A sinister looking insect is the wheel bug, a dark gray leggy creature with a wheel-like cogged ridge on its back and a wicked beak beneath its tiny head. It moves slowly along the flower stem, alert for a caterpillar or Japanese beetle into which it can sink its venomous stiletto. Humans who have carelessly handled a wheel bug can attest to the painful effectiveness of this weapon. Quite

as deadly is the tiger beetle that scampers along the path through the field, its green iridescent form gleaming.

The small round holes in the bare path are probably inhabited by the tiger beetle's larvae, the so-called "doodlebugs." Be very still and you may see one of the holes suddenly blocked by the round, flattened head of the doodlebug, its curving jaws hooked over the edge. Behind the head is a grublike body with a hook bulging from the back near the lower end. The hook anchors the larva in its tunnel when the jaws lock into a particularly powerful and reluctant insectival dinner.

Lest you think these predatory creatures have the best of it, remember that there are wasps that parasitize beetles, spiders that kill wasps, and birds that eat them all. What befalls the birds is another story, but in nature nobody really has the last laugh.

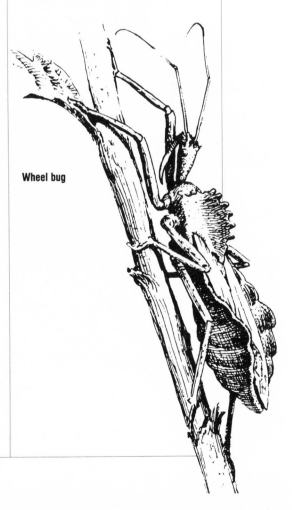

Wheel bug

Long-tailed salamander

Newt

Hellbender

SHY SURVIVORS

Now and then it happens. A fisherman reels in his jerking line and finds not a trophy fish, but a wriggling, thrashing slimy creature of such repulsive appearance that he fears to take it off the hook. But in spite of its two-foot length, its broad flat head, and its beady eyes, the creature is harmless. It is merely an outsized salamander, the kind known as a hellbender.

Impressive as it is, the hellbender isn't America's biggest salamander. That distinction goes to the amphiuma, an eel-like amphibian with tiny legs that prowls southern ditches, ponds and streams. Large ones grow to be 40 inches long. The smallest kind, hard put to reach two inches in length, is the pygmy salamander, found high in the southern Appalachians.

Most salamanders, however, measure between three and six inches long. Often mistaken for lizards, they differ chiefly in having smooth, unscaled skins and shorter, nail-less toes. Because they absorb most of their oxygen through the skin (many don't even have lungs), they must remain cool and moist. Some are largely aquatic, but those which are not hide in damp places beneath stones, logs and leaves, coming out only at night or on rainy days.

Except for a few species, salamanders mate in ponds, puddles and streams. On each side of the head the larvae have external gills. Normally these red, plumelike structures disappear before the larvae mature, but such thoroughly aquatic species as sirens, mudpuppies and waterdogs retain them throughout their lives.

Salamanders occur in endless variety. The long-tailed salamander is orange-yellow with a bold herringbone pattern. The green salamander's dark body is decorated with patches that resemble green lichens. The spotted salamander's black back is marked with perfectly round yellow dots. Several blind salamanders known from caverns in the South are white or pink and somewhat translucent. When young newts leave the water they are vermilion beauties known as red efts. When they return to mate they turn olive in color with tiny red spots. They acquire flattened tails for swimming and spend the rest of their days in the water.

Salamanders eat insects, crustaceans, earthworms, fish eggs and smaller salamanders. Except for the larger kinds, which can bite fairly hard, salamanders are quite defenseless. A few, notably the slimy salamander, exude a skin secretion that sticks to human hands like milkweed sap, but whether or not it is a deterrent to predators is not known.

Some salamanders are able to detach their tails when attacked. Once shed, the tail continues to lash furiously, drawing the attention of the assailant while the abbreviated amphibian quietly slips away. All in all, a salamander's best defense is probably its secretive nature, combined with a slippery body that wriggles frantically at the slightest touch.

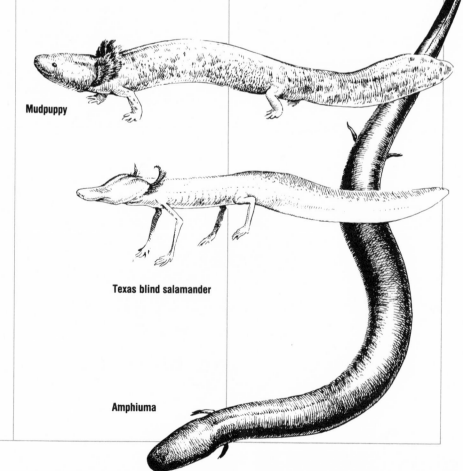

Mudpuppy

Texas blind salamander

Amphiuma

Caddis-fly *(above)* **and its trout fly look-alike**

THE AMAZING CADDIS-FLY

Were it not for the caddis-fly's habit of swarming around lights on a spring or summer evening, it would rarely be noticed. As it is, caddis-flies are usually mistaken for small moths—in spite of their long, hair-like antennae and wings that fold over their backs like a pup tent.

Their aquatic larvae, however, are well known. Called caddis-worms, caddis-creepers, stick worms, case-builders or strawmen, they are famous for the strange, portable "cases" or "houses" which they build.

Some species prefer weedy ponds; others like wave-washed lake shores. Some inhabit quiet stream eddies; others live out their larval span in swift-flowing water. The better the quality of water, the more caddis worms you find. And each builds a distinctive house—usually a tube of silk which it covers with the sand, pebbles, or plant debris among which it lives. The case not only protects its tender body, but often provides perfect camouflage to escape detection from predators.

Caddis cases come in a surprising variety. One common type is the stick case, a silky tube covered with small twigs and random lengths of plant stems. Another is stuccoed with coarse sand and pebbles; increasingly larger stones are added at the mouth as the inhabitant grows.

One species decorates its cases with pinhead-size snail shells, while another fashions slender, curved tubes coated with sand. Another species forms its case into a tight spiral like a snail shell only one-quarter of an inch across.

Most caddis-worms drag their houses with them as they search for the algae and other vegetation on which they feed. But not all species build portable houses. The strange *Hydropsyche* is one of these. Its predatory larvae live in pebble houses that are permanently attached to stones. Nearby they weave nets of silk which they stretch between stones or fasten to the edges of rocks. Guy-lines keep them taut and many are reinforced at their rims with twigs. When insects, water mites, or other small animals are washed into the net, the larvae, moored to its door by a silk lifeline, eases into the current and devours them.

When they finish growing, most caddis larvae attach their cases to a submerged rock, in some instances chewing the side out of the case to facilitate fastening it. Once secured, the larva closes the mouth of the case with a pebble or a screen of silk and pupates while wings, reproductive organs, and other adult features develop. A few weeks later it leaves the case and swims to the surface or to an emergent plant, where the pupal skin splits and the mature insect takes wing.

Caddis-flies in every stage of development are significant items in the diet of a fish. Trout dine on them regularly, and the sand, pebbles, and twigs found in trout stomachs attest to the fact that they habitually swallow cases and all. When the pupae leave their houses and swim toward the surface to emerge as adults, however, the fish go on their wildest feeding sprees. If this occurs during daylight hours, wise anglers can be seen removing their gaudy dry flies and searching through their fly boxes for drab patterns that look like caddises.

Brachycentrus caddis case

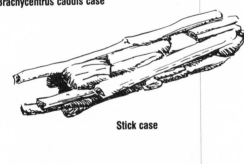

Stick case

Case made of strips of leaves

Caddis net

THE LIFE CYCLE OF A MOTH

The notorious moth that eats holes in clothes is the only moth many people know, but 10,000 other species are indigenous to the United States and Canada. Some are overlooked because of their nocturnal habits; others are mistaken for butterflies. Generally, if you see something at night, it's a moth; in the daytime, a butterfly.

Moths do resemble their diurnal cousins. Like them they wander about on four fluttering wings that derive their color and pattern from almost microscopic overlapping scales. Like butterflies, most moths have a tubular sucking organ called a proboscis.

On the other hand, distinct differences mark the two *lepidoptera*. Moths usually have hairier, more robust bodies than butterflies, and antennae that are feather- or awl-shaped, but never knob-tipped like those of the butterflies.

Instead of resting with their wings held vertically above their backs as butterflies do, moths spread theirs flat or hold them back like a miniature pup tent.

Moths become moths by passing through four stages—egg, larva, pupa, adult. The female gets the cycle started with her enticing scent, which some males can detect over two miles away! She lays her fertilized eggs on plants on the ground.

The larvae usually hatch within a few days. Some are tiny enough when full-grown to burrow between the upper and lower surfaces of a leaf. Others, like the seven-inch hickory horned devil, are huge. At this stage they are vulnerable to birds and many predacious or parasitic insects. While the Io moth larva, the bizarre saddleback caterpillar and others are protected by stinging hairs, many enjoy protective coloration. Certain inchworms, when disturbed, clasp a branch and stiffly elevate the body to look like a twig.

In the pupal stage, wings begin to form, chewing mouth parts change into proboscises, and reproductive organs develop. During this stage, some larvae spin silk cocoons for protection, each species making a distinct type. The giant cecropia attaches its silken pouch full-length to a twig or sprout. Woolly bears and other hairy caterpillars mix the hairs from their bodies with silk to form a felted cocoon.

Entering its final stage, the insect crawls from the cocoon.

Its abdomen is still elongated and the wings-to-be are mere crumpled stubs. Then the body pulsates and the stubs tremble as fluid is pumped through their veins. Within minutes these stubs unfurl and expand, until at last they are wings.

One of the most distinctive moths is the narrow-winged sphinx, often seen on flowers in the early evening. Noteworthy, too, are the tiger moths, many of which are spotted and streaked with yellow, black, orange, pink, brown and white. The little rosy maple moth wears a delicate pattern of pink and yellow. Yellow predominates in the color scheme of the lovely Io moth, whose hind wings present a huge pair of black-rimmed blue eyespots.

For sheer elegance, the luna moth reigns supreme. This furry creature has sweeping wings of a delicate pale green hue. Each purple-edged wing has a "windowpane" surrounded by a gold and black eyespot.

To see a luna moth up close is to behold a creature that many people regard as our most beautiful insect—an insect that is a colorful part of nature's grand design.

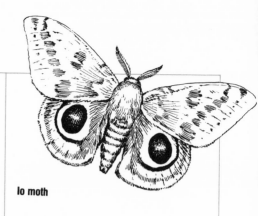

Io moth

Luna moth

Promethea cocoon

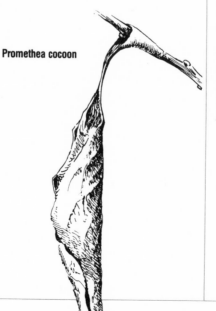

Saddleback caterpillar

FENCEROW REFUGE

Song sparrows and grasshoppers thrive
where fences shield vegetation from the plow.

Many farmers feel the fencerow is an outmoded nuisance—a bramble-covered barricade of rusting wire that cramps the style of their juggernaut tractors. Old fencerows are no better at penning livestock than a single strand of modern electric fence. So, why do fencerows remain?

For one thing, it's a job getting rid of them. Then too, a farmer just might enjoy hunting the rabbits they shelter, or hearing a bobwhite call from a fence post some June morning. He might notice that the snag in his fencerow provides a perch for the sparrow hawk that eats the mice that eat his crops. Indeed, he might recognize that an overgrown fencerow is one of the most amazing showcases of nature to be found anywhere.

During the past 12 years, I've lived within 100 yards of one such old line fence. It was not always a haven for wildlife. When its locust posts were first set in the ground and the woven wire was stretched and stapled into place 40 years ago, the ground beneath it was probably bare. Very likely, the first birds that perched on the new wires and left the seeds of pokeweed, blackberry, or poison ivy in their droppings gave the fence-row vegetation its start. Then milkweed seeds adrift on the wind probably settled at the base of a post.

It's not hard to visualize a red fox stopping to pull a burr from its fur and unwittingly planting the first burdock.

Little by little, new perennials joined the grasses and weeds. And eventually, trees were introduced by the activity of chipmunks, squirrels, or birds. Today, the varied vegetation shelters and feeds an infinite variety of wildlife that could not survive in the open farm fields on either side.

In its simplest role, the fencerow is a safe travel lane where wild things can journey unexposed to the dangers of open country. In springtime's mud, I find the tracks of skunk and groundhog; in summer's dust, the beetle's trail like stitching on a baseball, and feathers and footprints near a bobwhite's dusting place. In midwinter snows, I can track a foraging opossum and several gamboling cottontails.

But the vegetation along a fencerow does not just give wildlife a safe route to travel. It provides a place to live as well. Song and field sparrows, as well as bobwhites, hide their nests in the dense grasses just outside the first furrow. Cardinals, brown thrashers, catbirds, cuckoos, and indigo buntings nest among the concealing foliage and protective thorns of the blackberry canes and in the forks of dense shrubs. Robins, orioles, kingbirds and mourning doves build their nests in what may be the only remaining trees within a quarter-mile or more.

In such places, fencerows afford vital escape cover. Cottontails place great confidence in fencerows, for example. Even those born in fur-lined nests in the hayfields head for a fence-row as soon as they are able to travel. Bobwhites are partial to fence corners overgrown with honeysuckle, poison ivy or Virginia creeper. Ring-necked

pheasants baffle hunters by scurrying through a dense fencerow, then going along the far side until out of danger.

Even the posts and rails benefit the wildlife community. The post is the traditional dais for a singing male bobwhite, meadowlark or song sparrow. Rails are highways for gray squirrels commuting between woodlot and cornfield. They make great sun decks for lizards and blacksnakes. White-footed mice often cache their winter supply of seeds in hollow rails, while various moth larvae spin their over-wintering cocoons in cracks and crannies.

Abandoned woodpecker nest holes in fence posts have long been favorite nesting sites of the eastern bluebird, chickadees, titmice, flying squirrels and white-footed mice.

Fencerows are also refuges for burrowing animals. The woodchuck may do most of his feeding in adjacent fields because that's where the most succulent vegetation grows, but his home is the deep tunnel beneath the fence.

From an ecological stand-point, in fact, the chuck is one of the fencerow's most beneficial residents. Its abandoned dens provide homes for opossums, skunks and other creatures less able (or less willing) to dig for themselves. Foxes commonly appropriate chuck-holes for their nurseries—making a meal of the rightful owners if they are present to object.

Where farmland is devoted to one-crop fields kept "pure" by pesticides and selective herbicides, the varied plant life upon which a diversified wildlife population subsists could not exist, were it not for fencerows. And such diversity is needed to supply the needs of certain animals. Only on the milkweed, for instance, will you find the droll red milkweed beetles that roll over and play dead when disturbed or the monarch larvae and their exquisite green and gold chrysalids. Should I want to rear some beautiful promethea moths, I will find their cocoons in my fencerow only on sassafras or wild cherry twigs.

Other animal life is even more loosely associated with certain plants that thrive along old fencerows. Raspberries and blackberries lure box turtles from nearby woods. White-footed mice eat all manner of seeds and insects, but they, as well as chipmunks and many birds, are passionately fond of wild cherries and their seeds. Both pokeberries and mulberries, common fencerow "volunteers," are irresistible to many species of songbirds. Few of

A bobwhite interrupts its song and a flicker leaves its young in a fence-post cavity at the sight of a red fox, arch predator on the prowl.

The fox's quarry, the watchful cottontail, makes good its escape by ducking into the convenient tangle of weeds and brambles.

these creatures could thrive in the middle of a cornfield.

In nature's scheme of things, though, the plants along fence-rows attract plant-eaters—and they in turn attract predatory creatures. One stretch I know seems particularly inviting to robber flies, which perch on bare twigs and timothy heads to watch for insect prey. Goldenrod sometimes conceals a matching yellow crab spider waiting for the next visitor. Spider webs hang from twigs and stems to snare passing insects.

Other creatures devour plant-eaters in incredible numbers. Birds eat almost everything from robust katydids to microscopic leafhoppers. White-footed mice, chipmunks, snakes and sparrow hawks are all fond of grasshoppers. That insatiable consumer of vegetation, the meadow mouse, is the meat and potatoes diet of sparrow hawks, red-tailed hawks, snakes, weasels, foxes, screech owls and barn owls.

But even predators and parasites are controlled in turn. Shrews, those tiny, nearly blind, but extremely voracious predators that tunnel beneath the leaf mulch, are habitually killed, though not always eaten, by hawks, owls and foxes. Even the ultimate predator in the fencerow community, the fox, has its enemies: human hunters and trappers.

A fencerow is not a hiking trail. Its charm lies in its concentrated variety—so take it slowly, and try to see it all.

It's hard to conceive of a more educational nature trail than a fencerow. Although fencerows are becoming more scarce with each passing year, enough remain to provide countless hours of sleuthing.

Examine each new plant. Even the tiniest flowers are breathtaking when viewed through a magnifier. (A hand lens of eight or ten power will do.) Then search the undersides of leaves for the beautiful and bizarre in insect life. It, too, can be incredible under the lens. Examine the blooms of goldenrod and Queen Anne's lace, for they attract a variety of striking insects. Snoop to explore cavities in fence posts. A flashlight and a dental mirror make the search easy.

Old fencerows are worth saving—and they make a great Saturday morning nature walk.

Like many birds, the brown thrasher depends upon fencerows for feeding and nesting cover. Box turtles are fond of berries.

Ready to plunge into its den, the wary groundhog keeps an eye on the fox. Unused dens are taken over by opossums and others.

HIDING AS A WAY OF LIFE

Being swatted, sprayed, squashed or eaten is a fact of life—at least to an insect. And yet insects seem to thrive where sturdier creatures fail. Their means for survival are many. One is their habit of procreating just as fast as they are destroyed. Another is to fly, leap, or scurry away at the first sign of danger. But their basic technique is to escape detection in the first place.

Millions of insects survive because they so closely match their surroundings. Katydids, which live their adult lives surrounded by summer foliage, are green with wings that resemble leaves in texture and hue. Many foliage-eating caterpillars are green, and a number have markings that suggest the parallel veins of deciduous leaves. Insects that feed on conifer needles require a different camouflage. Some, like the larvae of the pine sphinx moth, display lines that make them nearly invisible among the needles.

Some insects escape notice by closely resembling other things.

Underwing moth in flight

Last summer I photographed a small gray and white moth resting in plain sight on a blackberry leaf in a fencerow. It so closely resembled the bird droppings on neighboring leaves that I had almost overlooked it.

Certain geometrids, or "inchworms," appear to be twigs as their prolegs grip a small branch and their body extends stiffly at an angle. Even the head looks like a terminal bud. An almost invisible "safety belt" of silk often holds them in place.

Another twig imitator is the walkingstick, a remarkably slender insect whose jointed, bark-colored body becomes a convincing twig at rest. Some insect species even have a notch in each foreleg to fit around the creature's head so when the forelegs are pressed together, they form a twig-like extension of the body.

Many treehoppers, midgets among insects, avoid detection simply by virtue of their small size. At least one species becomes even more inconspicuous by imitating a thorn as it clings, head downward, to a plant stem. A projection rising from its back heightens the illusion.

A delicate pink and yellow moth that habitually sips nectar from the deep blooms of the evening primrose often crawls into the closed flowers for a daytime nap. It doesn't matter that the moth can't withdraw completely out of sight, because the yellow wing edges that protrude look for all the world like additional yellow petals. Small geometrid larvae that feed on oxeye daisies cover themselves with bits of the flowers to hide from sharp-eyed birds.

Underwing moths are known for their colorfully patterned hind wings which are covered by the mottled gray forewings when the insect is at rest. In flight, the hind wings flash brilliantly, an enticing target for pursuing birds. Imagine the pursuer's confusion when the moth alights on a mottled gray tree trunk and the conspicuous flashes suddenly disappear.

The grotesque ambush bug uses camouflage for more sinister purposes. Blotches of dark and light coloring break up its body outline, making the insect inconspicuous as it lurks among the flowers of the goldenrod and Queen Anne's lace. An insect alighting on the platform of golden flowers realizes—too late—that the territory is already occupied.

Pine sphinx larva

Walkingstick

True katydid

Caterpillar matches foliage

Striped skunk—final warning

POTENT WEAPONRY

Bombardier beetle

Monarch

Viceroy

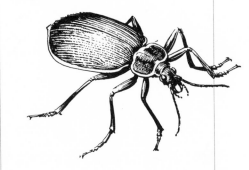

Caterpillar hunter

Last summer while hunting Indian artifacts, I noticed a black ground beetle hurrying over the uneven clods. Wanting a better look, I pinned it down with my finger, and the spunky beetle retaliated by squirting a tiny stream of fluid from its abdomen directly at me. The droplets fell short, but their pungency opened my head like ammonia, leaving me to wonder what predator could brave that potent concoction.

Many animals employ smelly, unpleasant or injurious secretions to repel their enemies. Skunks are the most infamous examples, of course. The fluid sprayed by a frightened or annoyed skunk is unmatched in the world of nature and beyond the imagination of those who have never experienced a direct hit—or even a near miss! Its choking, suffocating quality is bad enough, but should it enter the eyes, it burns like fire and can temporarily impair vision.

Many insects, on the other hand, depend upon their well developed repellents. The handsome green and bronze caterpillar hunter expels a spray of acrid fluid that stings human skin like concentrated nettles. The bombardier beetle works a little chemistry, combining several ingredients in a special hard-walled abdominal chamber to cause an audible explosion. The stinging mist is expelled with a "pop," right into the mouth and eyes of its attacker.

Toads have often been falsely accused of causing warts, but their truly offensive capability is rarely mentioned. A milky fluid, exuded by their warty skin, is extremely irritating to mucous membranes, disagreeable to the taste buds and actually poisonous. Rubbing one's eyes after handling a toad can produce a surprisingly unpleasant reaction. Most dogs that pick up toads are quick to drop them, and many are made ill by the exudation.

The toad has an insect counterpart in the blister beetle. Instead of merely tasting unpleasant, its body juices actually blister the skin. This powerful fluid's effect on the mouth of an animal or bird can only be imagined, but it is doubtful that the experiment is ever repeated.

The memory of such encounters is made easy through bright colors which mark many of the offending insects. For instance, most of the bitter-tasting insects which feed on milkweed (the milkweed bug, the four-eyed milkweed beetle, and the monarch butterfly, whose larva is a milkweed-eater) are boldly marked with orange and black. The system not only works, it also gives a measure of immunity to the viceroy, a perfectly edible butterfly similar in color and markings to the vile-tasting monarch.

FALL

When they must run, white-tailed deer can fly through the woods with incredible grace and speed.

Unlike other North American hoofed animals, pronghorns have no dewclaws.

Deer

Pronghorn

PRAIRIE SPEEDSTER

Different creatures are equipped to live in different places. Moose long ago adapted to bogs and lakes, deer to forests and brushlands, and bighorns to mountain peaks.

The pronghorn, America's smallest "big game" mammal, is beautifully fitted to life on the wide open prairies, deserts and high plains of our western states. Here its pale tan coloration, broken by bands and patches of white, blends into the sun-bleached surroundings. From a slight rise of ground, its telescopic eyes can discern an enemy long before that enemy becomes a threat. What's more, the pronghorn can escape predators by racing pell-mell over the gently undulating landscape.

The pronghorn's speed is its claim to fame. Long runs at 50 miles per hour and short bursts at more than 60 mph make it America's fleetest mammal. It is second only to the cheetah among all ground animals.

The pronghorn is built for speed. Its legs, long for its size, are slender but extremely strong. The haunches that drive those pumping hind legs bulge with hard muscles. Even the feet have been streamlined by the elimination of dewclaws.

The pronghorn's lung capacity is exceptional, and it runs with its mouth open, sucking in great quantities of air through a windpipe that is twice the diameter of a man's. Except when hampered by deep-crusted snow, it can usually outdistance any predator. By relay hunting in pairs, however, the swift coyote can occasionally exhaust and capture an adult pronghorn.

Despite its speed, the pronghorn is a poor jumper and must clear smooth fences by crawling under or squirming through. Woven or net wire fences are among its worst enemies.

When alarmed, pronghorns flare their rump patches into large, white rosettes, a danger signal that is seen by other pronghorns far and near.

Their sharp hooves are their major defensive weapons, but the bucks use their horns in autumnal fights for the possession of does. Once the breeding season has passed, the horn sheaths are shed, a process unique to the pronghorn among true horned mammals. The

The fastest mammal in the Western Hemisphere, the pronghorn can easily exceed our 55 mph highway speed limit for cars.

slender cores which remain permanently attached to the skull are already ringed with hair that will expand and harden to form the next year's horn sheaths.

Newborn pronghorns are "all legs," and for the first few days they are too unsteady to run from danger. Instead, they often sprawl on the ground to avoid detection. Within a week, however, they can easily outdistance any man and most dogs; within a year they become mile-a-minute sprinters.

Of the vast herds that once ranged throughout the American West, very few survived by the early 1900s. Ranchers, unwilling to share their grazing lands, destroyed them relentlessly, while some game departments permitted far too many of them to be harvested. Fortunately, by 1914, the animals had been given legal protection in all states, and in most states they responded remarkably well. Today, several hundred thousand pronghorns live in the West. Travelers speeding along the highways of western states now often see pronghorns from their cars. Though limited natural habitat will keep the lid on any appreciable expansion of its population, there is little doubt that the fleet pronghorn will roam the American prairie for many years to come.

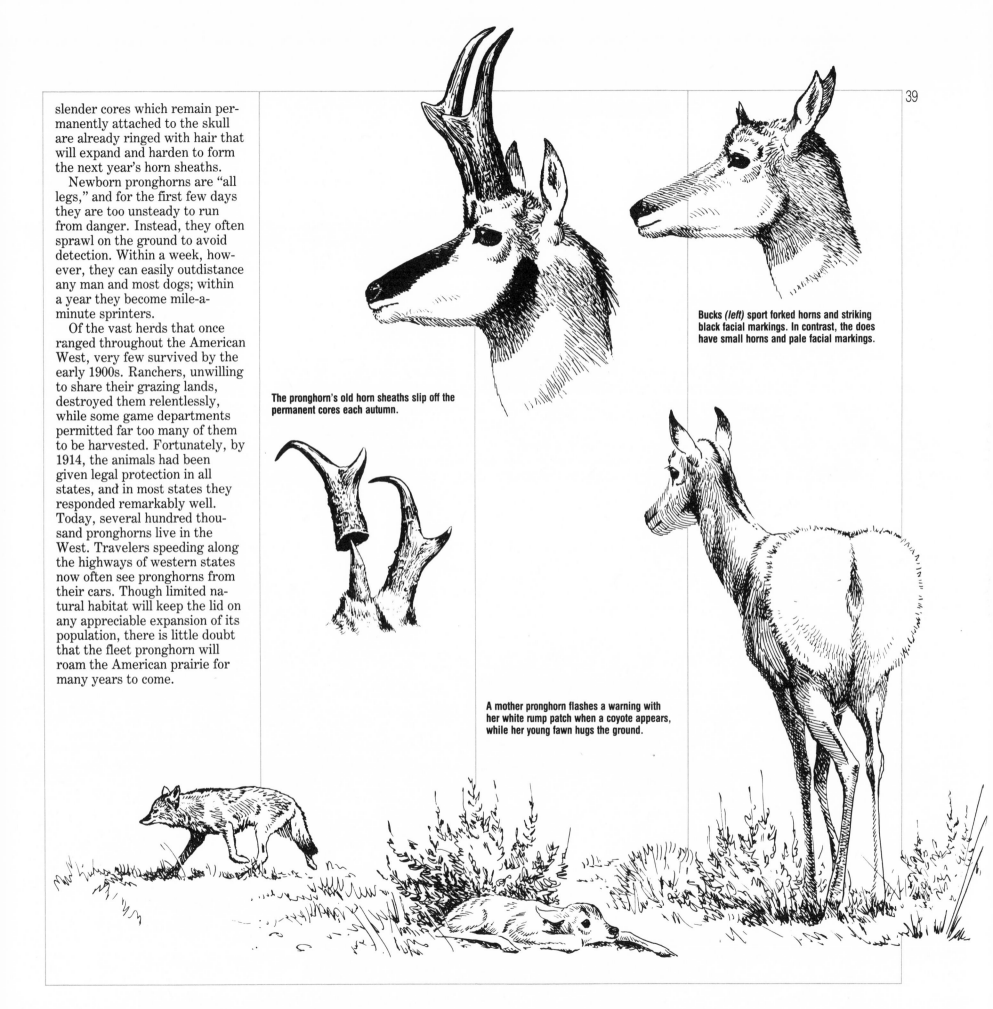

Bucks *(left)* sport forked horns and striking black facial markings. In contrast, the does have small horns and pale facial markings.

The pronghorn's old horn sheaths slip off the permanent cores each autumn.

A mother pronghorn flashes a warning with her white rump patch when a coyote appears, while her young fawn hugs the ground.

PRAIRIE DOGS

The first pioneers who crossed the short-grass prairies east of the Rockies in the 1800s were astonished to find sprawling settlements of stout little rodents. They called the creatures "prairie dogs" and labeled their vast colonies "towns." One town in Texas was said to cover 25,000 square miles and have 400 million inhabitants. Smaller colonies were found throughout the West.

Being dedicated diggers and insatiable eaters, the prairie dogs eventually wound up on a collision course with ranchers and farmers. Their numerous burrows were a constant threat to horses and cattle, and the wary prairie dogs chewed grasses and forbs right down to the bare earth to maintain a clear view of their surroundings. As a result, livestock in some areas found little to eat.

Most early measures to control the teeming prairie dogs didn't work, but with the introduction of easy-to-use poisons by the U.S. Biological Survey in the late 1800s, prairie dog numbers soon dwindled. Today widespread poisoning programs have been suspended. Even so, prairie dog populations are only

Prairie dogs are the major food of the endangered black-footed ferret *(above)*, whose slender body can swiftly follow every turn of the little rodent's tunnels in fast pursuit.

Burrowing owls often adopt abandoned burrows for shelter and nesting.

Prairie dogs are preyed upon by red-tailed hawks (shown here), prairie falcons, golden eagles, coyotes, and badgers.

RAISED MOUND PREVENTS FLOODING.

PASSAGEWAY TO ANOTHER MOUND PROVIDES ESCAPE HATCH AND VENTILATION.

WHILE MALE ON ENTRANCE MOUND GIVES TERRITORIAL CALL, A FEMALE PAUSES AT "LISTENING POST."

SIDE GALLERIES OFTEN CONTAIN REFUSE OR STORED FOOD, SOMETIMES DEAD PRAIRIE DOGS.

FEMALE VISITS YOUNG IN GRASS-LINED CHAMBER.

CHAMBER IS HIGHER THAN BURROW FLOOR TO ENSURE GOOD DRAINAGE.

a fraction of what they once were. The largest prairie dog towns are found in the Dakotas, Wyoming and Texas.

Prairie dog towns are frequented by a variety of other grassland animals, including several that hunt the burrow diggers. One such predator, the endangered black-footed ferret, depends entirely on the survival of the prairie dog for its own tenuous existence. Abandoned burrows, which stay cool during the summer and relatively warm in winter, provide valuable refuges for everything from spiders to rattlesnakes. Western meadowlarks and horned larks are often found singing atop prairie dog mounds, while many other birds prowl the towns for insects and weed seeds.

Prairie dog towns remind us of life in the Old West. Anyone who has ever ridden on horseback across flat grasslands—where the only sounds are the whisper of the wind, the distant song of a meadowlark and the staccato yipping of these rambunctious rodents—knows that the West would never be the same without them.

An insatiable appetite for vegetation keeps the prairie dog's view unobstructed—good insurance against sneak attacks by coyotes.

OWLS—AT HOME IN THE DARK

Owls play a special role in nature—controlling certain wildlife populations by night. Rats and mice, being nocturnal and abundant, bear the brunt of owls' predation, and in many areas these destructive rodents are held in check only by the tireless activities of "Old Hoot."

Owls would face an impossible task were it not for the fact that they are superbly equipped for catching prey in near darkness. Their eyes can gather an exceptional amount of light, thanks to their large size (a great horned owl's eyeballs are nearly as big as a man's) and the abundance of sensory cells in the retina which register light. The result is daytime vision equal to that of a human, and night vision that is probably ten times as efficient as our own.

Unlike other birds, an owl's eyes are positioned at the front of the head. Both eyes see the same object simultaneously (binocular vision), giving owls the depth perception necessary for zeroing in on their victims while in flight.

Owls are aided in locating hidden prey by their extremely acute hearing, the product of the largest eardrums among the birds. Experiments have proven that some species can catch mice in complete darkness, guided only by the faint sounds made by the little rodents.

Swooping down on its prey, the owl unleashes some of the most fearsome weapons of the bird world—strong, sharp, curved talons that hang onto the most squirming prey and quickly stab the life out of the sturdiest of animals.

The owl's hooked bill can tear food into bite-size chunks if necessary, but whenever possible owls swallow their prey whole.

When digestion has been completed, the bones, feathers, fur and other indigestible remains are ejected through the mouth in neatly packed pellets. From these leftovers, ornithologists have learned much about owls' food habits. Such knowledge reinforces the idea that owls are more than solemn symbols of wisdom or weird voices in the night. They are skilled predators whose services to wildlife and mankind are too often underestimated.

Great horned owl

Screech owl

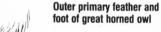

Outer primary feather and foot of great horned owl

ANTLERS—AN AMAZING CYCLE

The antlers that adorn the heads of males in the deer family seem to be as permanent as the animals themselves. They are, however, only temporary appendages. Each year they are shed and replaced with a new set.

Beginning in the spring as soft, swollen pads on the skull, they soon lengthen into club-like structures. While growing they are covered with a fuzzy skin called "velvet," beneath which blood circulates through a network of vessels. The tips are bulbous; the entire antler is tender and easily damaged.

In two months they begin to show the general shape of the antlers to come—in some instances mere "spikes," in others elaborately branched or palmated affairs. Four to six weeks later they reach full size.

At full size, they undergo a surprising transformation. Beneath their furry covering the antlers harden and the blood supply stops. The velvet, now dead and dry, peels off in strips, aided by the buck's vigorous rubbing against bushes and trees. The antlers are now bone-hard, with pointed tines.

For a few weeks in autumn, antlers resist the punishment of head-on rutting season clashes. Then one day, when the mating and fighting urge has passed, they suddenly drop from the

Bull moose

buck's head, leaving only a pair of bony bases from which next year's set will grow.

The cycle is the same with deer, moose, elk, and caribou. Although the moose's huge palms may span 76 inches and weigh 70 pounds, and the elk's majestic beams measure six feet or more in length, they attain these impressive proportions in the short period of three or four months, making them the fastest growing animal tissue known.

What happens to the shed antlers? Within a few months they have usually been reduced to unrecognizable fragments by decay and the incisors of mice, squirrels, and porcupines, to whom they are a welcome source of salt and calcium.

Antler growth of white-tailed deer

Ready for instant flight, a white-tailed buck tries to identify the source of a faint but suspicious sound in the distance.

THE INDOMITABLE WHITE-TAILED DEER

Five deer lie chewing their cuds and dozing in the mid-winter sunshine. Last night, they fed in an old orchard at the bottom of the mountain, then threaded their way up the snowy slope to bed down before daybreak. If they appear relaxed, it is with good reason. They have chosen their bedding grounds with care. Rising thermals will bring them the scent of anyone following their trail. Their beds face in all directions to cover all approaches and good cover surrounds them.

In the distance, a twig snaps, the sound muffled by the snow. Instantly, all ears are cocked in that direction. Muscles tighten, nostrils flare. Footfalls, barely audible, mark the progress of the unknown intruder, and at the first glimpse of him through the trees the little band is on its feet, bounding up the mountain and out of sight. The hunter never knew they were there until he crossed their tracks.

That scene is repeated countless times every deer hunting season, and it helps explain why the white-tailed deer is considered the nation's most successful big game animal.

The taming of the American wilderness was disastrous for most big game animals. Cutting the forests, plowing the prairies and grazing the foothills—combined with uncontrolled year-round hunting—wiped out several subspecies and nearly exterminated titans such as the bison of the plains and the grizzly south of Canada. The one big game animal that bounced back with vigor wherever it was given some protection was the white-tailed deer. In many areas, in fact, it became more numerous in the second growth forests, with their abundant browse, than it ever was in the virgin forests.

Game management played a major role. Most states finally halted such destructive practices as the killing of does and fawns, shooting over salt licks, and night shooting with artificial lights. Refuges were established and stocked from areas of relative abundance. Fees collected from newly established hunting licenses were used to hire wardens. So well did these measures succeed that today in many areas overpopulation of deer can be controlled only through additional hunting. If any big game species can survive close to civilization, the white-tailed can.

On the surface, the white-tailed deer seems an unlikely candidate for survival. Except for the northern races, it is our smallest and most delicate-looking native deer. One subspecies, the endangered key deer, seldom exceeds 50 pounds. In parks and preserves, white-tailed deer are as tame as cows, and even where hunting is permitted, they often become quite trusting during the closed season when they become accustomed to seeing people.

But truly wild white-tailed deer, living on their wits and stamina, are something else again. Not only are they quick to sense danger, they usually react without panicking.

First, they try to identify each suspicious sound or object. Aware that a running deer can blunder into trouble, they prefer to sneak away silently, when feasible, and they run only until out of immediate danger. In dense cover, they often remain motionless, relying upon their inconspicuous color to hide them.

When they must escape, white-tailed deer can fly through the woods with incredible grace and speed, bouncing jauntily or flat out running, whatever the situation calls for. Rocks and brush are no hindrance. I've seen them clear nine foot "deer-proof" fences with ease.

Few large mammals are as adaptable as the white-tailed deer. Pronghorns require large open grazing areas. Mountain goats are confined to lofty mountains. But white-tailed deer can subsist in small farm wood-lots, in southern swamps, in

scorching deserts, along mid-western river bottoms and on the Rockies themselves.

Typically an eater of mast and browse, the white-tailed deer has adapted to eat agaves in the desert, potatoes on hill farms and crown vetch in road-side and pipeline plantings. Its stealth and nocturnal tendencies enable it to hide out in a small patch of brush by day and emerge under cover of darkness.

Few states are more highly industrialized, more populous, or more crisscrossed with paved roads than Pennsylvania. Each year, many deer are killed by autos alone. Free-roaming dogs are known to kill many as well. And yet, enough white-tailed deer still remain for hunters to take several thousand each year. Considering that a doe produces only one or two fawns each spring, vast numbers must elude hunters, autos and dogs.

What can threaten the white-tailed deer's future? The destruction of habitat, for one thing. Adaptable as it is, the white-tailed deer simply cannot live in shopping centers, browse on airport runways or co-exist with power mowers. In areas

less susceptible to development, the white-tailed deer's over-abundance is in itself a threat.

Wintertime, with its reduced vegetation, lower temperatures and, in the north, deep snows, is the critical period. If the white-tailed population is too dense, the deer may exhaust winter food supplies and destroy the food-producing potential of the wintering area for years to come. "Browse lines"—visual evidence that the deer have eaten all the twigs they can reach—appear and fawns, having less "reach," will be first to starve. Artificial feeding is rarely practical. Consequently, many wildlife management experts believe that controlling the population by hunting is the best solution so far. Surely it makes more sense than condemning so fine an animal to waste away.

White-tailed deer, one of America's most often seen wild animals, are at home in various habitats from deserts to mountains.

Mere cold holds no danger for white-tailed deer as long as they get adequate natural food. Artificial feeding is seldom practical.

In autumn the male bobolink acquires a streaked winter costume similar to the female's. In spring it is molted and exchanged for a brown-barred plumage (top).

THE CHANGING OF THE GARB

Come late summer and early fall, bird identification becomes a challenge. The male scarlet tanager, once incredibly red, turns olive green. The black-bellied plover becomes white-bellied. And the male bobolink exchanges his dashing black and white attire for a streaked coat of brown.

Why these seasonal changes? Perhaps because the conspicuous hues and patterns that were so useful to males in courtship displays attract unwanted attention from predators at other times. More importantly, most color changes are caused by the shedding of certain feathers—a process called molting—and replacing them with feathers of a different color. All birds undergo a nearly complete molt, usually in late summer.

Male wild ducks undergo a nearly complete, but short-lived molt in the middle of the summer, during which their brilliant attire is replaced by so-called "eclipse" plumage closely resembling that of the drab female. On both hens and drakes, all wing flight feathers are shed simultaneously, rendering the birds temporarily flightless.

About a month later, when new pinions have restored their powers of flight and made concealing coloration less vital, the eclipse plumage gives way once again on the drake to the elegant breeding plumage. Oddly enough, only drakes of the northern hemisphere undergo the eclipse molt.

As spring's brown feather tips wear away, the male bobolink's handsome breeding plumage is revealed.

White-tailed ptarmigan in autumn (left), and in winter white to match snowy surroundings.

Some birds, like the tanager, molt again in the spring and regain their breeding colors. One familiar example is the male English sparrow, whose black bib is concealed by gray feather tips that erode in the spring.

Ptarmigan, those hardy grouse of the far north and the high west, undergo three molts. In winter, their immaculate white coats match their snowy surroundings. In spring they acquire a patchwork plumage of brown and white to mimic the lingering patches of snow. In summer they become somewhat duller to blend with the lichens, mosses and rocks of their bleak environment. Possibly no other birds can claim so complete and effective a wardrobe.

Both these birds are black-bellied plovers. One appears in its pale winter plumage *(left)*, the other in its boldly marked spring dress.

A mallard drake in full breeding colors *(top)* contrasts with the same drake in eclipse plumage *(bottom)*. Note the absence of wing flight feathers.

The male English sparrow's black bib is hidden *(right)* until gray tips wear off of black feathers *(below)* to reveal it.

Instead of diving for prey like their brown cousins, white pelicans surround schools of fish in shallow water and scoop them up.

Gray squirrels can elude many enemies by hiding behind tree trunks, but this tactic doesn't work when hawks hunt in pairs.

HUNTING TOGETHER

Predation is a fact of life in the natural world. It can be the instantaneous act of a thrush snatching a beetle, or a long, drawn-out drama of a fox stalking a rabbit. But where the quarry is too elusive or too dangerous for a one-on-one confrontation, different hunting techniques must be employed. For many predators, this means joining forces with others of their kind in a group effort.

A single white pelican, for instance, would stand little chance of scooping up small fish in the open water because the fish could dash in almost any direction to safety. Instead, the big birds assemble on the water in a curving line and swim shoreward, flailing the surface with their wings to herd the fish into shoreline shallows. There, confused and surrounded, the fish are gathered up in the pelicans' capacious beaks.

The gray squirrel often reacts to danger by scurrying around a tree limb, keeping inches of solid wood between itself and the attacker. But this ruse rarely works against red-tailed hawks and other buteos that often hunt in pairs or family groups. Hiding from one hawk merely exposes the squirrel to the other, and only by reaching a tree cavity can it find safety.

Coyotes use a variety of co-operative hunting techniques. Naturalist Ernest Thompson Seton once watched a coyote sneak ever closer to a prairie dog while the rodent's attention was diverted by another coyote brazenly trotting back and forth in plain view. This prairie dog escaped the stalker's final rush, but the coyotes' technique is often effective. Other people have seen swift pronghorns zigzag or race in semicircles to avoid pursuing coyotes, only to be ambushed by another coyote hiding in their path.

Of all North American predators, however, wolves are probably the ultimate practitioners of group hunting. By working together, they can overwhelm such large creatures as the moose, an animal that may weigh as much as ten wolves and can kill its pursuers with a single kick.

Often, a wolf pack will sneak as close as possible to its prey without being detected, then once discovered, will quickly close the gap. Should the moose stand its ground, the wolves will usually go on their way. But if it takes to its heels, the chase will soon be on. Avoiding the lashing hoofs, some of the wolves will tear at the running animal's flanks and rump, inflicting considerable damage. Another wolf usually races ahead and fastens its teeth onto the moose's throat or, more often, on the bulbous nose, directing attention away from those attacking the hindquarters and slowing the animal's flight.

The moose's size usually precludes a quick kill. Instead, the moose must be relentlessly harassed, torn and weighed down until the cumulative effect is death, probably due to a combination of loss of blood, exhaustion and shock.

Predation is never pretty, but if the burgeoning populations of prey species were left unchecked, they would not only destroy their own food supply but the food and cover of many other animals as well.

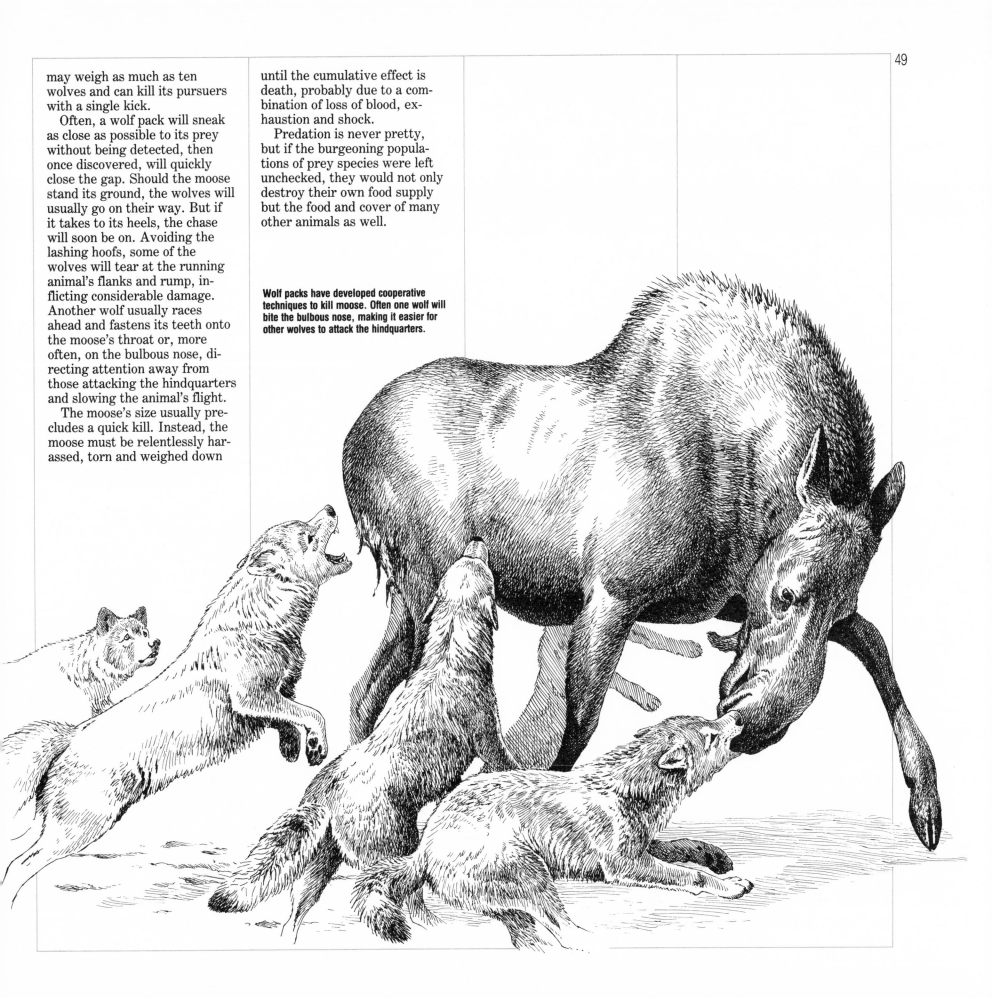

Wolf packs have developed cooperative techniques to kill moose. Often one wolf will bite the bulbous nose, making it easier for other wolves to attack the hindquarters.

The white underside of the white-tailed deer's "flag," raised in flight, disappears when the deer stops and lowers its tail. Without the flag, the deer fades from sight.

When threatened, many insects feign death and drop to the ground, hidden in the weeds.

Red foxes have been said to run from pursuing hounds for days. They can lay a difficult trail with ease—taking to water, jumping off logs, and doubling back.

ESCAPE!

Because predation is a threat to nearly all animals, techniques for escape are endlessly varied. The grasshopper, its hind legs laced with hard muscles, launches itself from a standing start with the suddenness of a snapped trap, too fast for the eye to follow.

When the ruffed grouse senses discovery is inevitable, it gets a head start by bursting from concealment with a thunderous roar of wings, startling its would-be captor into temporary immobility. Slippery and squirmy hellbenders are almost impossible to hold onto, while some snakes make themselves undesirable with foul-smelling glandular secretions. Rabbits duck into briar patches to elude the fox, and squirrels take to the trees.

Protective coloration is the key to survival for many creatures. Others depend on hard shells, sharp spines, teeth and talons, stinging cells, or repellent sprays. But for many animals, escape is still the most practical recourse.

Many escape techniques that have evolved over the ages in response to natural enemies are surprisingly effective against humans. Consider, for example, the classic escape patterns of the white-tailed deer. A white-tailed buck, startled by human scent, tosses his tail erect, revealing the snowy white underside. Nearby deer may have missed the smell of danger, but they see the signal and follow the buck out of the area, flying their own "flags" as they dash away through the woods.

The human stalker hadn't seen the deer until they took off at his approach. Now he tries in vain to keep the bounding forms in sight as they flicker between tree trunks and through underbrush, but his eyes are drawn instead to the dancing white banners. Then suddenly they, too, disappear. The deer have merely stopped, dropping their tails to conceal the white undersides as they watch from what they consider to be a safe distance. Their gray-brown bodies are almost invisible against the forested background.

The flashing white underside of the tail, which communicates a warning and keeps the individual deer together in flight, has saved many a white-tailed's hide. True, it sometimes betrays a hidden deer, but more often, it adds a distracting element that persistently draws attention away from the deer itself.

Other examples abound. A rabbit's zigzag flight foils hunters as well as hawks and owls. A mountain goat's ascent of lofty crags often puts it out of reach of people as well as grizzlies. And the bonefish's sizzling dash for the safety of deeper water, perfected to escape fish-eating birds and predacious fish, fouls up all but the finest reels, jamming their drags and popping fragile leaders.

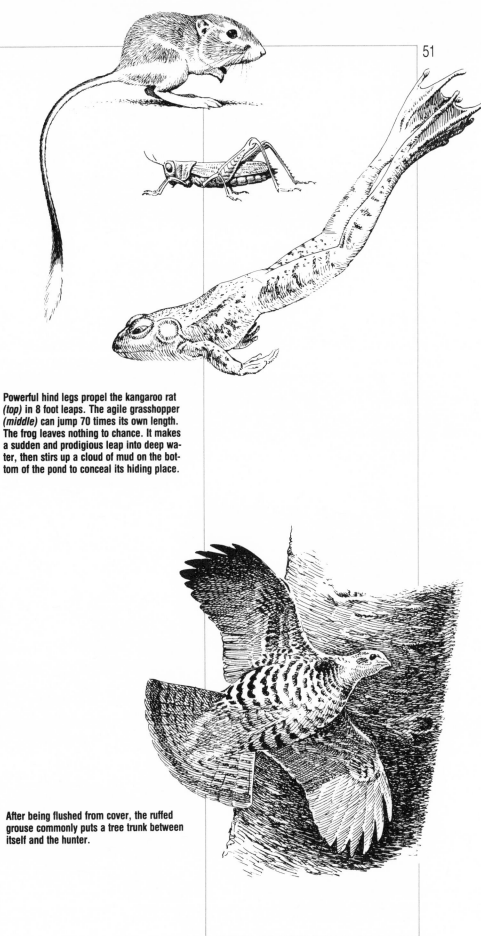

Powerful hind legs propel the kangaroo rat *(top)* in 8 foot leaps. The agile grasshopper *(middle)* can jump 70 times its own length. The frog leaves nothing to chance. It makes a sudden and prodigious leap into deep water, then stirs up a cloud of mud on the bottom of the pond to conceal its hiding place.

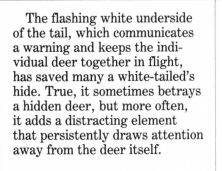

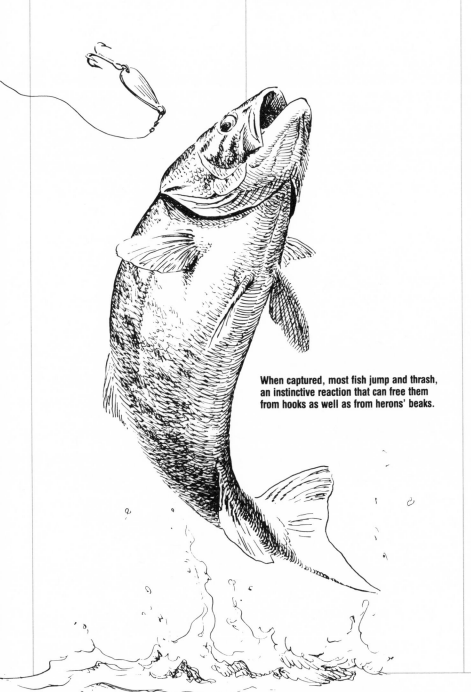

When captured, most fish jump and thrash, an instinctive reaction that can free them from hooks as well as from herons' beaks.

After being flushed from cover, the ruffed grouse commonly puts a tree trunk between itself and the hunter.

MAKE A FEEDING STATION

You can convert your backyard into an excellent wildlife habitat by providing food, water and cover. Even before the shrubs and trees mature, you can make your backyard a gathering place for birds by establishing a wintertime feeding station this fall.

Feeding birds can be as simple as scattering birdseed on the snow, but a variety of food will attract a larger assortment of birds, and simple, properly constructed feeders will keep food available in any kind of weather.

Basic foods are beef suet, seeds or grain, and fruits. Brown creepers, woodpeckers, nuthatches, chickadees, and other insect-eaters will relish the suet. Grosbeaks, cardinals, titmice, finches and chickadees are fond of sunflower seeds, while mixtures containing such small seeds as hemp, millet, rape and flax will appeal to a host of seed-eaters from siskins to mourning doves. Add raisins and chopped apples to your menu to please mockingbirds, waxwings and others. Crushed dog biscuits, chopped hard-boiled eggs and cooked spaghetti are a few more to try.

Don't toss bread crusts for the birds. Bread's food value for birds is near zero and it tends to

This feeder was reserved for small birds by using closely spaced dowels.

fill them up rather than keep them hungry to search for more nutritious food.

Place most feeders near shrubbery or other cover, but for horned larks and other open country birds spread fine seeds in open areas cleared of snow.

To lure timid birds close to the house place a trolley feeder near distant cover and move it closer each day.

Birds will discover food sooner if the roof is left off a feeder at first. It can be installed for protection from the weather after the birds become accustomed to using the feeder. The 20- to 24-inch tilting metal disc beneath the tray is a guard against squirrels.

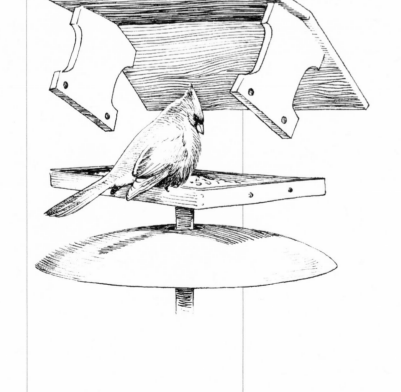

In very cold climates birds' eyes can freeze to metal holders. These substitutes are safer. Bore holes in a log section (left) and pack with suet, or hold a chunk of suet (center) with zigzag binding. Suet hung in an onion bag (right) is another alternative.

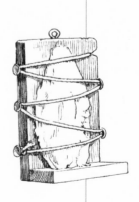

TALENTED BATS

Bats have been the subject of some pretty weird myths and superstitions, but even the most imaginative folklore cannot match the facts. The more we learn about these nocturnal creatures, the more amazing they prove to be.

Their most unique accomplishment is their ability to fly, for in all the world there is no other mammal with this gift. Flying squirrels can glide, of course, but they are not capable of true flight.

A close look at the bat's wing reveals a framework of delicate bones that corresponds almost perfectly to those of the human arm and hand, in arrangement if not in proportions. The hind feet are small, little more than hooks for hanging head downward from a perch or rough surface.

Bats are most active in the half-light of evening, though some species occasionally venture out during the day.

Bats have notoriously poor eyesight but employ a form of sonar to locate their insect prey. In flight the bat emits a continuous stream of high frequency squeaks that are inaudible to the human ear. The echoes that bounce off nearby objects reveal the distance, size, and nature of the objects so perfectly that the animal can not only zero in on small insects but can also avoid colliding with twigs, wires, and foliage while doing so.

The young, usually one or two, are born naked and helpless except for an instinctive determination to cling tightly to anything they touch. Some species hang their babies on cave walls in "nurseries"; others carry them on foraging flights.

Contrary to popular belief, bats are almost completely harmless. They do not carry bedbugs nor entangle themselves in women's hair. Tropical bats, especially the blood-eating vampires, can carry rabies, but in the north this danger is almost non-existent. Left alone they're happy to go about their business of sweeping the evening sky clear of insects.

Long-eared bat hanging from cave wall.

Bats are crawlers not walkers.

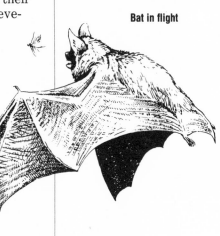

Bat in flight

WINTER

Wildlife is still here,
it's just more aloof,
harder to find.

THE LONG SLEEP

Many wild creatures have neither the ability nor the instinct to migrate to a warmer climate for the winter, nor can they find enough food or warmth to sustain them until springtime. Their only recourse is to greatly reduce their need for food, and this they do by becoming more or less dormant during the winter.

Some, like the woodchuck, the jumping mouse, and innumerable cold-blooded creatures, enter a deathlike sleep with the advent of cold weather. The woodchuck's body temperature sinks to a few degrees above freezing, and its respiration and heart rate slow to four or five times a minute. Its body feels cold to the touch and rough handling will not arouse it. This state of suspended animation is called hibernation.

Some animals stop short of hibernation. Bears seek out nooks where they can sleep undisturbed, but their pulse, breathing, and body temperatures are not greatly diminished. They are easily awakened, and the cubs are born during this period. Raccoons, skunks, and others not so handicapped by cold or food shortages sleep

Chipmunks are deep sleepers, but they occasionally awaken to feed on caches of nuts and seeds they stored earlier in the fall.

Frogs hibernate in the mud of pond bottoms.

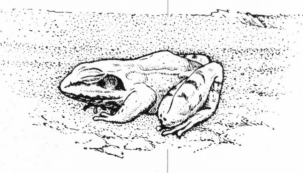

This motionless furry ball is a woodchuck hibernating in its underground bedroom.

for days or even weeks while the weather is severe, but venture abroad when it moderates.

But even the true hibernators need some energy during the long winter. For this reason all creatures anticipating the long sleep stuff themselves with food in the fall, storing energy in the form of fat beneath the skin. Woodchucks become comically pudgy, snakes increase their girth, and even insects build up fat beneath their chitinous shells. It is this fat that nourishes life until their natural food is again available and the weather turns warmer.

Some bats fly south in the fall; others hibernate in caves. The mourning cloak butterfly *(right)* hibernates in sheltered crannies and reappears on the first warm days.

Dens among the rocks sometimes house hundreds of hibernating snakes.

Black bears are less fussy than their grizzly cousins about their winter quarters.

WHEN LIFE GOES INTO HIDING

Midwinter's landscape, especially the icebound pond beneath its blanket of snow, seems bare and lifeless. But in summertime, as any pond-watcher knows, few natural areas are so rich in animal life. Millions of aquatic insects and fish lurk among emergent plants; turtles and watersnakes are on the prowl. What happens to these teeming hordes as the pond prepares for winter?

Like most wildlife habitats, a pond reaches its lowest carrying capacity in wintertime. The water is then but a few degrees above freezing; food is at a minimum, and the oxygen supply beneath the icy surface diminishes. To conform to these limitations, excess animal life must somehow be purged and the remainder given the means to survive.

Probably the greatest exodus from a pond—one that begins in springtime and continues into the fall—is the emergence of matured aquatic insects whose immature forms have been living in the pond. Caddisflies, may-flies, dragonflies, damselflies, midges, and craneflies crawl from their nymphal shuck. Then they mate, and if uneaten by fish, frog or bird, deposit a batch of eggs.

Many animals are eaten by predators. Insects eat zooplankton; small fish eat insects; larger fish devour kingfishers, and watersnakes and snapping turtles eat small fish. Big fish fall prey to fishermen or sometimes to ospreys and otters.

The cooling of the water in early autumn is in itself conducive to predation. After spending the "dog days" in a nearly torpid state, the largemouth bass respond to cooler temperatures by feeding ravenously. Watersnakes, which shunned the broiling sun and moved about only at night and in early morning, now hunt minnows and frogs around the clock. The increased activity reduces the pond's population, and it fattens the predators against the lean months ahead.

As water temperatures drop lower, the larger cold-blooded denizens grow less active. Bass and sunfish retire to the deepest part of the pond and wait out the next few months in a state of almost complete dormancy.

Snapping turtle digging in for the winter.

Frogs and turtles burrow into the muddy bottom to hibernate. Their oxygen requirements are slight. Indeed, the frogs absorb enough directly through their skins, and the turtles "breathe" through an abundance of blood vessels in their ventral openings. Watersnakes, unfitted for underwater respiration, hibernate for the most part beneath the overhanging banks.

Water striders, those unsinkable acrobats of the surface, disappear into shoreline crevices or pass the winter beneath logs or stones on shore. Most aquatic insects winter among debris on the pond's bottom.

The notable exceptions are the diving beetles, back swimmers, and related aquatic beetles, which often remain active throughout the cold weather by carrying an oxygen supply with them. Backing up to the infinitesimal layer of air immediately beneath the ice, they raise their wing covers and trap a bubble against the tip of the abdomen before returning to the bottom.

A pond in winter may appear "dead," but in truth its inhabitants are merely dormant.

Diving beetle descending with air supply.

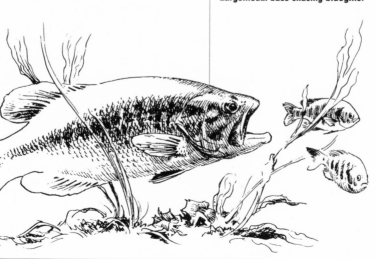

Largemouth bass chasing bluegills.

WHEN PLANTS MARK TIME

Springtime's green-up doesn't just happen; nature has been preparing for this event for months. The red oak acorn, tucked beneath its coverlet of dead leaves since last autumn, began as a single, microscopic cell that was fertilized by sperm from a pollen grain last May. Then began interminable dividing into more cells—the process by which it became an acorn and by which, with luck, it will eventually become an 80-foot giant oak tree.

But now, as winter marches on, it merely bides its time. Like other seeds, from the dustlike seeds of the orchids to the robust black walnut, the acorn contains an embryonic plant. With the coming of

Skunk cabbage

spring, most seeds absorb additional moisture and split their shells. A simple sproutlike extension grows upward, often topped by the cotyledons, or seed leaves, which contain the stores of food for the burgeoning embryo until its new roots and foliage become functional.

Many mature plants, especially perennial herbs, survive the winter only as underground structures—roots, rhizomes, tubers or bulbs. In addition to their function of anchoring and supporting the stems and leaves while alive, these structures also contribute to the spread of the species. New plants spring from trailing rootstocks. Bulbs separate and sprout. Tubers, widely separated from the parent, send up shoots from their "eyes."

More important, these buried parts become wintertime pantries. All summer the leaves made sugar and stored it as starch and sugar in the roots, tubers, rhizomes or bulbs. This food will nourish the new plant when it emerges in the spring.

Some young plants, usually biennials (which require two growing seasons to produce seeds) have another way of getting the jump on their neighbors. They do this in the fall by forming winter rosettes, which look as though some furtive gnome had grabbed a plant's roots and pulled them down into the ground, leaving the plant's foliage radiating from a common center on the surface. This ground-hugging arrangement

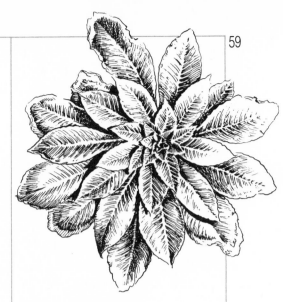

Rosette of evening primrose

protects the plant from the rigors of winter, and plants thus usually stay green until spring. When warm weather arrives, the stem lengthens, making it a full-sized plant.

Does the method work? We must assume it does, for its most conspicuous exponents, such as the thistles, evening primrose, chicory, wintercress, the goldenrods, and the mustards, are among our most indomitable weeds. It appears that plants, in common with nearly all wildlife, must get the better of winter to survive.

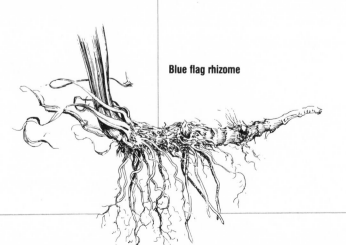

Blue flag rhizome

Crossbills are nearly as acrobatic as parrots while feeding on hard-to-reach cones.

Many ornithologists credit artificial feeding with bringing the evening grosbeaks back to the Northeast with unprecedented frequency.

INVADERS FROM THE NORTH

When winter arrives in all its full-blown fury, some species of birds are occasionally driven out of their customary ranges in search of food further south. Then, these "obscure" invaders can often be encountered almost anywhere. Snow buntings and pipits prefer windswept lake shores, beaches, dunes, and open fields, where they can glean weed seeds from snow and bare ground. When lemmings disappear from the tundras, big snowy owls gravitate south to hunt meadow mice and similar fare in fields and dunes. Ponderous rough-legged hawks, too, adopt open country south of their summer range.

But other birds of prey prefer different situations. The rare and bizarre great gray owl, for example, keeps a hungry eye on meadows near dense stands of trees. The flashy goshawk haunts the forests, where it occasionally ambushes a ruffed grouse or red squirrel. Fence-rows and scattered trees in farm country attract the northern shrike on its every-fourth-year southern sojourn.

Because their curiously crossed mandibles are modified for opening cones, the crossbills are seldom found far from their favorite conifers. The white-winged crossbills seek out hemlocks and spruces; the red crossbills prefer pine cones. Pine grosbeaks like conifer seeds, too, but you might also find them munching apple seeds or mountain-ash fruits.

Of all the invaders from the North, the one best known is probably the evening grosbeak. No need to look afar for these handsome birds. Their preferred winter habitat is the nearest feeder with sunflower seeds.

Like most birds of the tundra, the snowy owl rarely perches in trees.

In winter, rough-legged hawks often adopt open country south of their summer range.

A study in gray and black, the goshawk is a handsome, fearless predator.

Snow buntings sometimes travel in flocks of several hundred birds.

THE FORMIDABLE PORCUPINE

Few North American mammals can waddle through life with the calm self-assurance of the porcupine. Only the fierce fisher, a flesh-eating animal of the marten family, has learned to attack it with impunity. Other predators—the great horned owl, the lynx, the cougar and the wolverine—occasionally do a porcupine in, but more often than not pay dearly for their brashness.

The porcupine's quills are its security. Specialized hairs, they are loosely attached to the hide on its back, sides, and tail. The black tips are sharp as needles and are covered with hundreds of microscopic barbs. When

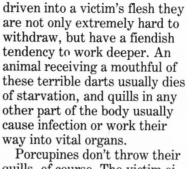

Porcupine gnawing tree bark

driven into a victim's flesh they are not only extremely hard to withdraw, but have a fiendish tendency to work deeper. An animal receiving a mouthful of these terrible darts usually dies of starvation, and quills in any other part of the body usually cause infection or work their way into vital organs.

Porcupines don't throw their quills, of course. The victim either comes in contact with the bristling body or gets in the way of the lashing tail.

When discovered far from the refuge of a tree or den, the porcupine's first reaction is to turn its back to danger and duck its unprotected head between its legs or into a convenient cranny. A network of muscles stands the back quills on end, and the clubby tail is cocked to slap at anything that comes close. Should the porcupine decide to move to safer quarters, there's no stopping it. The porcupine *backs* toward its goal, clearing the way with its flailing tail.

Normally the porcupine minds its own business, which consists chiefly of eating. During the summer months it feeds on a variety of plants, but in colder weather its diet is mostly the inner bark of trees. Evergreens, birch, aspen, and beech seem to be its favorites. Its home range is extremely small, and a porcupine will sometimes remain in one tree for several weeks, oblivious of the weather, while rasping off patches of bark.

Unfortunately, the porcupine is also passionately fond of salt, a craving that frequently gets it into trouble. Canoe paddles and ax handles flavored with perspiration are quickly reduced to tooth-marked fragments. So are aluminum frying pans, pack frames, snowshoe laces, and the furniture in cabins.

There are probably as many theories about how porcupines mate as there are about how

On the defensive

baby opossums get into the pouch. The simple truth is that the female is careful to keep her tail and quills out of the way, and copulation takes place in the conventional manner.

But there normality ends. Usually only one young is born, which in itself is remarkable for a member of the prolific rodent family. What's more, this infant often weighs more than a pound, which is considerable for a mother weighing from 12 to 20 pounds. A black bear weighs only half as much at birth.

The newborn porcupine is well developed. Its eyes are open, its hair is dark and thick, its quills are fully formed and up to an inch long. The quills are soft at birth, but within an hour or two harden to become the formidable weapons for which all porcupines are respected.

Tip (enlarged) of the quill

CHANGING TO WINTER CLOTHES

The advent of winter calls for a change of clothing for wildlife as well as for humans. Warmth is the prime requisite, and the natural winter coats of wild animals and birds of the north are warmer for their weight than anything humans have been able to manufacture. Dead air is the miracle insulator; by retaining body heat it makes life possible even in the polar regions.

Winter fur and feathers are designed to achieve this end. The familiar northern white-tailed deer, for example, wears a summer pelage of straight, slender hairs. The hairs of the winter coat, on the other hand, are not only stout and crinkled, but hollow as well, each containing its own dead air cells. A scanty undercoat of fine wool adds warmth.

In birds, insulation has reached near perfection. Feathers are amazingly effective air traps. With the addition of a dense layer of down, such birds as sea ducks and penguins can be blasé about the coldest temperatures. Their plumage is waterproofed with secretions from their oil glands, so they can swim in near-freezing water with impunity.

Birds can also regulate the degree of insulation by compressing their feathers to drive out the trapped air in warmer weather, and fluffing the feathers when it's cold.

Some mammals change to a different color in winter. The white-tailed deer swaps its summer red for grayish-brown. The gray squirrel, whose thin summer pelage is generously tinged with brown, assumes a clear gray pelage in winter.

A few mammals don a pure white coat for mid-winter camouflage in the snow. The well-known ermine is nothing more than a northern weasel that has replaced its brown summer hairs with white ones.

The snowshoe hare not only turns white in winter, but its huge feet are made even bigger by a fringe of stiff hairs that creates wonderfully effective snowshoes. One bird, the ptarmigan, turns nearly or completely white to match its snowy habitat. It, too, acquires snowshoes by growing a fringe of feathers on its toes. Likewise, the ruffed grouse's snowshoes are formed by a comb-like fringe of scales that edge the toes during the cold months.

Ruffed grouse foot in winter

Ptarmigan in winter plumage _(left)_ and summer plumage

Varying hare in winter

HOLIDAY HAVEN

A backyard without wildlife is like a stage without actors, and the illusion of emptiness is heightened when winter strips the hardwoods of their leaves and hides lawns and flower beds beneath the first snowfall. Fortunately, wintertime is also the best time to attract wildlife to your backyard. Not only will wild birds and mammals respond more willingly to your overtures when food is scarce and trees are bare, but it is personally rewarding to help them through their roughest season.

Plans for attracting winter wildlife must be tailored to the condition and location of your backyard, giving special consideration to existing cover. Newly built homes with their spindly infant trees and shrubbery offer little concealment for most game birds and mammals. But small songbirds of many species naturally gravitate to such open areas, and other wildlife will become regular winter visitors with the proper inducements. The illustrations here suggest some devices for making your backyard inviting. Many more will suggest themselves as you begin work on your own plot.

Feeders should be numerous and offer a variety of foods to lessen competition among birds. The window sill feeder (*below, left*) features a divided hopper to hold two different kinds of feed. One side might be filled with sunflower seeds for the ever hungry and often belligerent evening grosbeaks. Smaller mixed seeds, possibly with nut meats or crushed peanuts, might be put in the other half for the smaller, less aggressive birds. The central placement of the feeder itself keeps birds of different sizes apart.

The woodpecker and its acrobatic friends like to eat from hanging feeders that discourage greedy starlings, house sparrows and several larger birds that dislike the swinging and swaying. One feeder is a commercially made plastic suet bag, two are log-type suet holders (bottle caps nailed to short sections of log are filled with beef suet), and the other is a plastic bowl filled with sunflower seeds. Half a coconut shell is another widely used seed or suet receptacle. If no sizable trees are available, these feeders can be hung from a planter "tree" or a trellis or lamp post.

The feeder on the post is enclosed across the front with closely spaced dowels that admit

Curved metal strips direct the feed through slots onto the tray.

This windowsill feeder dispenses coarse seeds from one compartment, fine feed from another. Smaller birds congregate on one side, larger birds on the other.

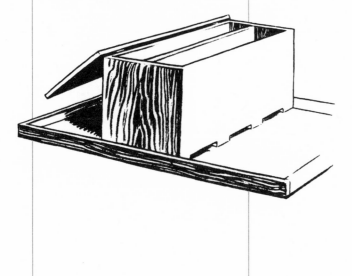

Squirrels can't raid this feeder mounted on an iron pipe and shielded by a tilting disc.

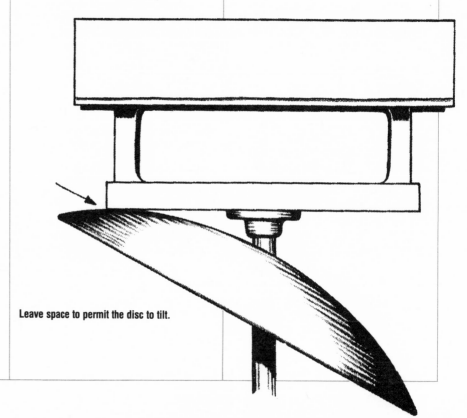

Leave space to permit the disc to tilt.

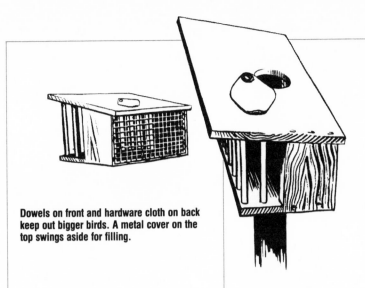

Dowels on front and hardware cloth on back keep out bigger birds. A metal cover on the top swings aside for filling.

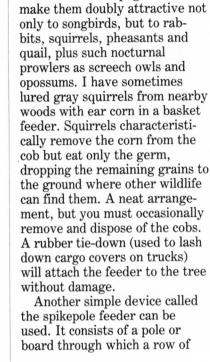

small birds but keep out the larger ones. The hardware cloth stapled across the back permits the birds to see through the structure, preventing that hemmed-in feeling that most birds distrust.

Discarded Christmas trees will provide useful cover in otherwise bare surroundings. You can fasten them to young leaf-less trees (with strips of cloth that won't rub through the bark) to provide escape cover near feeders and birdbaths. Or you can decorate them with strings of popcorn and stale doughnuts, and coat the boughs with a mixture of melted suet, seeds, nut meats and crushed peanuts.

Wildlife needs water in wintertime as much as in summer. An aquarium heater, available in pet stores, keeps water in the birdbath free of ice. When installing such heating devices, use heavy-duty outdoor cords and seal all connections with plastic tape.

Older backyards in rural or suburban settings with larger trees and dense shrubbery nat-urally harbor a larger wintertime population of wildlife than the recently landscaped yards. The addition of devices similar to those on these pages will make them doubly attractive not only to songbirds, but to rabbits, squirrels, pheasants and quail, plus such nocturnal prowlers as screech owls and opossums. I have sometimes lured gray squirrels from nearby woods with ear corn in a basket feeder. Squirrels characteristically remove the corn from the cob but eat only the germ, dropping the remaining grains to the ground where other wildlife can find them. A neat arrangement, but you must occasionally remove and dispose of the cobs. A rubber tie-down (used to lash down cargo covers on trucks) will attach the feeder to the tree without damage.

Another simple device called the spikepole feeder can be used. It consists of a pole or board through which a row of spikes has been driven. It is fastened between two supports and ears of corn are impaled on the protruding spikes.

Cater to suet-lovers by hanging feeders from the branches of a nearby tree. In squirrel country you'd better hang such things with wire, rather than cord, which is tempting to the incisors of the busybody rodents.

Wary pheasants and rabbits prefer to stay close to cover. But they will respond to the security of a row of discarded Christmas trees leaning against a taut wire and fastened in place. Trim off the branches on the underside to make more

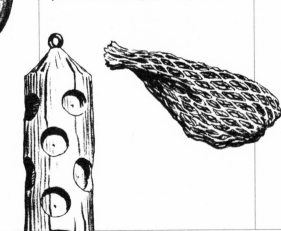

Left to right: Coconut shell is a favorite for holding seeds; holes bored in log section are packed with suet; hanging net bags hold suet.

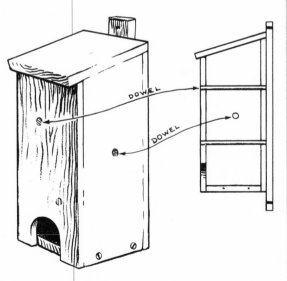

Roosting boxes have dowels for perches. Entrance holes are at the bottom.

room and fill the openings near the top. Scratch feed, scattered in a thin line from the ringnecks' accustomed haunts, lures them to the larger supply beneath the evergreens. Rabbits will follow the alluring aroma of apples, vegetable trimmings and alfalfa hay, probably making the first visits under cover of darkness. Christmas tree shelters should be constructed to permit easy escape from dogs or natural predators. Remember to drive the necessary stakes into the ground before it freezes or you'll have to fasten the wire to trees or clothesline posts.

Roosting places are often at a premium in wintertime because of the influx of cavity-nesting (hence cavity-roosting) birds. Leave a few birdhouses in place all winter. A nest box which is home to a flicker family in springtime may house a screech owl during the winter. Bluebird

houses are perfectly acceptable as winter quarters to chickadees and titmice.

The nocturnal mammals are usually neglected, yet they are among the most interesting and entertaining creatures that might come to a feeding station. Flying squirrels (which might winter in your bluebird house) love peanut butter smeared on tree limbs; they romp there at night. Raccoons and opossums are readily attracted to cat and dog food, fish, meat and fruit. Divide the bait into bits that can't be carried away en masse. Place it where it won't make a mess and where the nighttime visitors can be watched beneath a light that can be turned on from inside the house. Even-

Left to right: Bottle caps holding suet; a plastic bowl filled with sunflower seeds.

tually they will ignore the light and your wildlife watching will become a day-and-night affair.

Now is the time to build feeders, drive stakes and line up promises of your neighbors' used Christmas trees. Plan now to make Christmas a merry one for wildlife. It's the year's best opportunity to give a little and receive a lot.

Basket feeder *(left)* is framed with heavy wire. A spike-pole feeder *(below)* is easily made from discarded lumber.

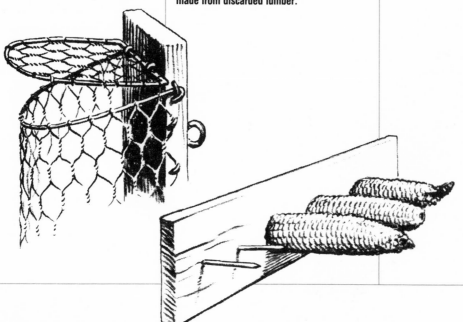

EVERGREENS FOR WILDLIFE

For centuries lovingly decorated Christmas trees have brought holiday cheer to households throughout the Christian world. But in their natural environment, our pine, spruce, fir and hemlock trees give still greater gifts to their wildlife neighbors.

Cover—encompassing both concealment from enemies and shelter from the elements—is perhaps the most important gift of the conifers. Experienced hunters are well aware of the concentrations of ruffed grouse, deer, rabbits and other game found in evergreen thickets, especially in wintertime when the deciduous trees are bare. Even such typical farmland species as bobwhites and pheasants take advantage of the dense pine stands found in farm country.

Some forest species are able to thrive in agricultural areas only because of the concealment offered by conifers in small woodlots. White-tailed deer are particularly clever at living most of the year under the very nose of the farmer—sleeping under his evergreens during the day and feeding in his fields at night, unseen and unsuspected.

Where wildlife is concerned, cover can be a matter of life or death. Bobwhites can be practically wiped out by a severe northern winter—or spared by the friendly shelter of dense pine. Many a ruffed grouse has saved its skin by dodging behind the thick foliage of pine or hemlock for both nesting and roosting. In winter long-eared owls spend the day in evergreens, safe from the eyes of the pesky crows and jays, sometimes in flocks of up to 50 birds.

Few cover types are so heavily used by nesting wildlife. Not only do hawks, robins, mourning doves, owls, cardinals, and other birds choose to build their nests in pine, hemlock, and spruce, but squirrels and white-footed mice do the same.

Other wildlife species depend upon the conifers for food. Pine grosbeaks get the seeds by cutting the cones to bits with stout, sharp-edged bills, while the piñon jay, named for its passion for piñon pine "nuts," finds most of its fare on the ground beneath the trees.

The red squirrel nearly dissects the cone, nipping off one scale at a time to reach each pair of seeds. The scales and cores which accumulate beneath its favorite perch are testimony to its fondness for conifer seeds.

Other parts of the trees also have food value. Deer browse the tips of hemlock twigs, and

White-tailed deer in his evergreen hideout.

spruce grouse eat the needles and buds of northern spruce. Porcupines gnaw great patches of bark from pine and hemlock to obtain the tasty inner bark, often staying in the same tree for a week.

In some areas evergreens are stripped by black bears that have developed a fondness for the inner bark. Bark beetles also eat bark, sawfly larvae eat the needles, and borers devour the wood itself. Certain birds (kinglets, red-breasted nuthatches, numerous warblers and pileated woodpeckers) feed largely upon the insects that live in these trees.

Our enjoyment of tinseled trees is a fleeting thing, but "wild" Christmas trees, in the true yuletide spirit, keep right on giving throughout the year.

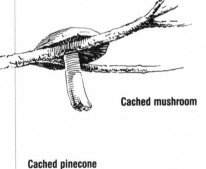

Cached mushroom

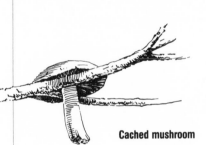

Cached pinecone

Franklin's spruce grouse

Mule deer buck

Egg masses of tent caterpillar *(right)* **and praying mantis**

White-footed mouse

A CHRISTMAS HIKE

When the gifts have been exchanged and the sumptuous dinner reduced to crumbs and calories, it's all too easy to spend the rest of the day in overstuffed boredom indoors. A Christmas hike is a better idea—better for the body and better for mind and eye grown dull with inactivity.

The apparent dearth of interesting things to see keeps many folks from enjoying the outdoors in winter, but a closer look will prove otherwise.

An abandoned fencerow near my home is a good example. At first, it appears to be nothing more than an out-of-kilter trail of ancient posts and rusting barbed wire, alternately held up and pulled down by briars, weeds, vines and trees. But in its 300 yards are surprises aplenty, even in late December.

The trail begins beneath overhanging trees in a thickety area where my arrival always draws sharp protests from a pair or two of excitable cardinals. In turn, the red squirrels fume intolerantly. They've half-filled an old catbird nest in the green briars with wild cherry seeds from which they extracted the kernels, and stashed a pint of unopened pits in a knothole in the corner post. Here and there a black walnut rests in the crotch of a limb, jammed there by the red squirrels as insurance against leaner days.

Overhead, wild cherry twigs wear bracelets of tent caterpillar eggs, "varnished" with a hardened liquid to keep out the weather. The frothy blobs on the blackberry canes beneath them are the egg masses of praying mantises. Made of nature's foam plastic, these blobs provide perfect insulation for the scores of eggs in their center. Tiny slits in a row down the face of each mass are papery valves through which the hatchlings will later force their way to the outside world.

A weathered bluebird house on the tallest post along the trail looks deserted and empty from the outside, but the interior has been stuffed with grasses, leaves, and rabbit fur. When I part the fluffy mass I find a pair of white-footed mice, calmly regarding me with huge black eyes and twitching whiskers.

Tracks in the snow betray a band of pheasants moving ahead of me. They take wing suddenly and noisily, scattering a flock of tree sparrows from their feast among the weeds. At the end of the fencerow, the snow beneath an alligator-barked tree is dimpled with fallen fruit—blackened and wrinkled persimmons whose incomparable musky flavor is at its best after the first December snows.

But Christmas hikes need no fencerows. A half-mile of river shore is an equally interesting, but different, world. Sleek mergansers dive for fish in the current, and mallards sleep on the ice around a patch of indigo water. You might surprise a muskrat tunneling through the snow to find his favorite greens, or spot a red-tailed hawk keeping watch from a tall sycamore.

A Christmas hike is feasible and fun almost anywhere. Floridians can choose between beach, woods or swamp. In the foothills of our western mountains, you might encounter big game herds driven down from the high country by winter storms. Or rosy finches and other birds that move to lower elevations when things get rough near the timberline.

All over this land, outdoor places are begging for attention during the winter months. If more holiday gourmands knew what they were missing, the Christmas hike might soon become an American institution.

IT'S A GAME OF TRACKING

For every wild creature that is seen or heard, a hundred pass by unobserved. Only when we notice their rambling footprints in the snow do we realize how much activity takes place when we're not there.

One day last month I strung my own footprints across the

Opossum tracks

Tracks of a ruffed grouse landing in snow and walking away

fields and woods that reach to the river. I learned, among other things, that a raccoon had moved into a hollow tree in Weaver's woods, three deer had bedded down in the pines, and more cottontails had survived the hunting season than I thought possible. I found the oak woods crisscrossed with gray squirrel tracks, and the footprints of a ringneck rooster and three hens in a cornfield.

"Reading sign" tells us not only who was there but also what they were up to. One winter I saw where a black bear had ambled across a knoll and slid down a steep slope on his seat. Later he left his tracks around a deserted cabin; I could tell he had stood on his hind legs to peer in a window.

Foxes leave unmistakable impressions where they crouch and spring on meadow mice in the grass. Grouse tracks leading from a trough in the snow show where the bird slid to a soft landing and walked away. A rabbit leisurely made his way to a briar patch, where slash marks and thorns strewn over

White-tailed deer

Deer running

the snow reveal that he felled a blackberry cane and ate all but the prickles. Apparently something frightened him, for he crossed to the safety of a slab pile in eight-foot bounds.

Identifying the maker of the tracks is the first step in reading sign. Study the size and shape of dog and cat footprints for a start, then move on to the ubiquitous rabbit and squirrel. Deer tracks are common and distinctive. Note that elk footprints are larger and blunter; moose are *much* larger. The opossum displays a distinctive "thumb" on his hind foot, while muskrats, otters, and beavers show hind feet adapted for swimming. The claws of foxes, wolves and coyotes, like dogs, show in their footprints; those of the cat family do not. Skunks, beavers, muskrats, raccoons, bears, rabbits and squirrels usually imprint the entire hind foot to the hock in the snow.

Footprints often show up in a distinctive pattern. When the deer, the canines, and the cats are walking or trotting, they leave evenly spaced footprints in a nearly straight line. Rabbits, on the other hand, progress by hopping, bringing the long hind feet ahead of the front feet.

A raccoon's typical gait pairs the footprints, one hind foot beside one front. The skunk,

Elk

Moose

Black bear tracks

loping along, often plants his four feet in a diagonal line.

A tracking snow is the traditional medium for sign reading, but just as much can be learned from a mud flat, a sandy beach, or a dusty road. A lane behind our house attracts a horde of wild things. Birds scratch holes in the dry soil for dusting, and the long, slim footprints of pheasants, the smaller ones of quail, and the X-shaped prints of flickers tell who they are. The winding trails of caterpillars, the beetle tracks like stitching on a baseball, and the occasional smooth "tire track" of a small snake add variety.

Apparently the old lane is a playground for rabbits at night, for their tracks run up and down the ruts in self-obliterating layers. Showers will occasionally put an end to the dust, but the resulting mud keeps its records with even better fidelity—a fascinating book to those who learn to read it.

A red fox pounces on a mouse in the snow, gulps it down, and trots on his way. →

Skid marks show where the fox turned to race after a cottontail.

Here a red squirrel dug up a buried pine cone and ate it.

The rabbit runs for its life. →

The lucky cottontail reaches the safety of a groundhog hole just inches ahead of the snapping jaws of the pursuing fox.

← A doe has left her daytime bed for a brief snack. She watches the activity with mild interest, then resumes feeding.

STORIES IN THE SNOW

The drama illustrated on these pages took place late one winter day in a sunny corner where fields and woodlands meet. The cast of characters includes a red fox, a ring-necked pheasant, and several supporting players.

As a rule, the daily travels of wild animals are among nature's best kept secrets. But when snow blankets the countryside, each and every footfall is recorded and displayed like words in a book. Woods-wise folks can read that book. They know that the line running like stitching across the snowy pastures was made by a foraging fox. They recognize the slim-toed tracks of the pheasant and the flat-footed prints of the raccoon.

In another time, when hunting and trapping were a way of life, people obviously had to know how to read tracks and signs. Today, such knowledge is less vital, but it still provides insight into the habits of our wild neighbors and increases our enjoyment of the outdoors.

Identifying the maker of the tracks is the first step. If you don't have experience, several books can help. Determining the age of the tracks is more difficult, and figuring out what the animal was actually up to requires experience and the gift of applied imagination. You must try to visualize the animal as it made each footprint; you have to see its body stretch or hump, speed up or slow down, to produce those erratic marks.

Details are important. Slight differences between hind- and fore-prints must be recognized. Slightly different spacing between individual footprints should be noted; they mean a change in speed. Gradually, the picture takes shape, like a movie composed of split second frames, until finally the creature's actions are reconstructed from the evidence in the snow.

A mile of fox meanderings has been compressed to fit these pages, cutting out some uneventful stretches and retaining a number of interesting diversions. Notice how each quick turn, crouch, sudden rush or twisting leap is signified by a break in the evenly spaced pattern of trotting footprints.

Note the gashes made by the birds' wingtips on takeoff and the tail feathers braking for a landing. Without the accompanying interpretation these could be difficult to decipher, but unless their meaning is discovered there is little excitement in following the trails.

Track reading can be fun anywhere there is snow. In a north country spruce forest, the tracks of moose, wolves, fishers,

snowshoe hares and spruce grouse might be encountered. Rocky Mountain foothills might be laced with the trails of elk, pronghorns, jackrabbits, coyotes and magpies. Even suburban areas reveal a surprising number of inhabitants, ranging from dogs and cats to pheasants, raccoons, and opossums.

The roll call of inhabitants, of course, is only the beginning. Uncounted adventures are recorded across the face of each pristine field and woodland. But for every line that is read, a thousand chapters will be erased by the next snowfall.

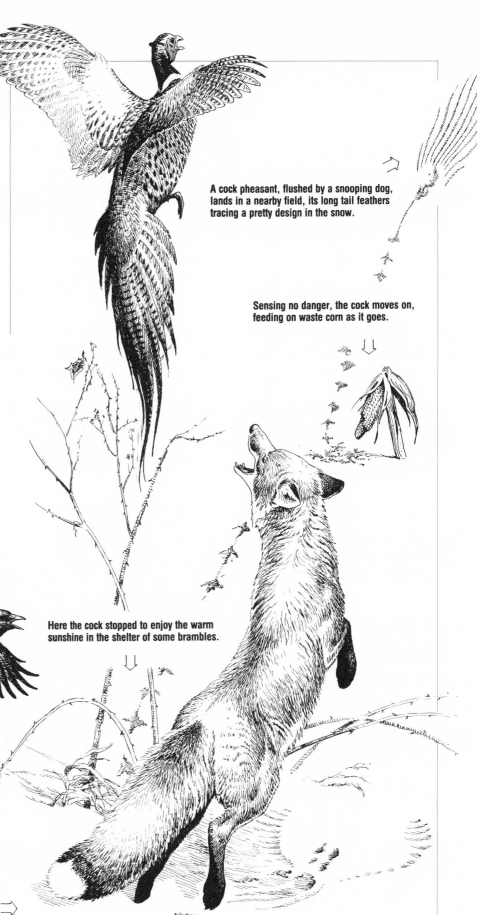

A cock pheasant, flushed by a snooping dog, lands in a nearby field, its long tail feathers tracing a pretty design in the snow.

Sensing no danger, the cock moves on, feeding on waste corn as it goes.

Here the cock stopped to enjoy the warm sunshine in the shelter of some brambles.

A crow takes wing and follows the fox, taunting it with loud, snarling caws.

Getting wind of the pheasant, the fox sneaks closer, then leaps. But the pheasant, alerted by the crow's fussing, escapes the rush.

THE WINTER SEASHORE

Winter brings a dramatic change to the salt-spray world of beach and dune. Where bathers thronged to beat last summer's heat, and shore birds migrated in seemingly endless flocks, the scene along many northern seashores is now one of relative solitude.

But don't let first impressions fool you. Wildlife is still here—it's just more aloof. Those dots strung out on the distant bay are scaups, redheads and a few "cans." That winding tidal creek hides a dozen black ducks just beyond the second bend.

A short-eared owl, digesting its breakfast of voles and rice rats, stares unnoticed from atop a muskrat house across the marsh. Plump dunlins swarm over a mud flat. Depending upon the latitude and weather, one might find a few lingering great egrets, a troupe of tiny semi-palmated sandpipers or a turnstone poking about.

On the dunes, camouflaged horned larks and native spar-rows search the sand for wind-strewn seeds. Occasionally a Lapland longspur from the north or a dickcissel from the prairies is seen. Impeccable herring gulls, handsome black-backed gulls and perhaps a few ring-bills hang on the updraft above the outermost dunes or pad flat-footed along the sand.

In the lee of an overhanging dune, an offshore wind leaves a pocket of comparative comfort from which to watch the lower beach, the incoming waves and the ocean beyond. Sanderlings in winter gray scamper back and forth, first pursuing, then flee-ing, the waves. A great blue heron solemnly waits for its dinner with feet awash. Beyond the breakers, a flock of brant ride at anchor near a red-throated loon in pale winter dress, and far out a flock of surf scooters drifts across the shimmering backdrop like a cloud of smoke.

Early cold spells can force some birds southward, to the delight of southern bird watchers, but local birding can suffer. With fish, crabs and

Human beach strollers can often spot whelk egg cases (below) and horseshoe crab shells (bottom) that have been cast up by waves.

The short-eared owl keeps a lookout for rice rats, voles, or similar creatures to eat.

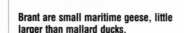

Brant are small maritime geese, little larger than mallard ducks.

In wintertime, sanderlings exchange their rusty plumage for pale gray.

other prey moving into deeper water to escape the cold, many birds must search out the small schooling fish that swarm near the surface far out to sea.

However, a storm at sea may bring them back, driven shoreward by lashing east winds. With them might come the unexpected—little gulls, kittiwakes, murres, shearwaters, jaegers, harlequin ducks, even Old World great cormorants or tufted ducks—far from their usual haunts. Gannets wheel on immense outstretched wings just beyond the breakers. Scoters, eiders and huge flocks of old squaws move closer to shore, and cormorants trade up and down the coastline in the troughs between the waves. Sprightly Bonaparte's gulls appear everywhere.

When the east wind dies, the birds may be gone, but the watcher will hold on to the memory. He is convinced, despite red nose and watery eyes, that winter is the choice time to visit the sandy edge of the sea.

Gannets are spectacular, soaring on outspread wings or dropping 100 feet to the sea.

Bonaparte's gulls often feed in the surf.

Adult

Immature

A great black-backed gull (below left) patrols the beach while a ruddy turnstone adeptly flips a shell in its search for food.

Numerals printed in **boldface**
indicate illustrations.